HEALTHY AS A HORSE

Discover How a Forgotten Framework of
Care can Transform Your Horse's Health

ANGIE WELLS

Equine CEO
PUBLISHING

Equine CEO
PUBLISHING

Equine CEO Publishing
PO Box 404
Fruita, CO 81521

ISBN # 978-0-578-65888-9

WARNING AND DISCLAIMER

To my soul horse, Pokey. The inspiration of this book and the work I do every day to improve the health and quality of life for horses.

TABLE OF CONTENTS

Introduction   1
But Horses Aren't That Healthy   1
That One Special Horse   2
Wake Up Call   6
Blinders Off and Dukes Up   7

Part 1 - Foundation   10

Chapter 1 - The Elephant in the Horse Industry   12
Let's Talk About It   12
What is Health?   14
The 8 Laws of Health   16
Choosing Which You Want to Magnify   20
Illness and Disease Have a Clear Process   21
Summary & Action Steps   23

Chapter 2 - The Best Nutrition for Your Horse   25
The Infamous Complete and Balanced Nutrition   25
Spotting Synthetics   27
Nutrition Basics to Keep in Mind   30
Selecting a Healthy Base   37
Simple Nutritious Whole Food Choices   39
Whole Food Choices to Avoid   43
Cellular Health and Function   45
Summary & Action Steps   47

Chapter 3 - The Real Pathway to Health   49
The Equine Health Pathway   49
The Three Amigos of Equine Digestive Health   50
The Fundamentals of Your Horse's Pathway to Health   53
Summary & Action Steps   55

Part 2 - Firewalls   56

Chapter 4 - Overcoming the Pesky Parasites   58
Nature's Design and Plan   58
Control versus Treatment   59
Common Parasites for Horse Owners to be Mindful Of   61

Customizing a Parasite Control Plan for Your Horse   63
Natural Options for Parasite Control   64
External Parasite Concerns   66
Summary & Action Steps   66

**Chapter 5 - The Insiders Guide to the Natural View of   68
Vaccination**
How Does Someone Believe That?   68
Beyond Stories   71
When Driven By Fear…   73
The Immune System Basics   75
Review the List of Invaders You're Injecting into Your   77
Horse's Bloodstream
What Options or Alternatives Do You Have?   78
Summary & Action Steps   80

**Chapter 6 - The Secret Impact of the Metal in Our   81
Horses' Lives**
No Hoof, No Horse and Straight From the Horse's Mouth   81
Bits of Information You Likely Never Knew   82
Is Natural Hoof Care Sustainable for Your Horse?   84
Too Much Too Soon   86
Summary & Action Steps   87

Part 3 - Finishing Touches & Customization   89

Chapter 7 - What Tends to Get Overlooked   91
Don't Shoot The Messenger   91
You Can't Skip or Stuff Your Horse's Emotions and   94
Expect Health
What You Use on The Surface Counts   95
Summary & Action Steps   97

Chapter 8 - Natural Modalities to Enhance Health   98
No Need for Fancy Gadgets   98
Summary & Action Steps   104

Chapter 9 - Customization   105
Why Cookie Cutter Approaches to Health Fail   105
The Remarkable Synergy of Your Horse's Body   106
Summary & Action Steps   111

INTRODUCTION

BUT HORSES AREN'T THAT HEALTHY

Maybe, you read the title and thought "But my horse isn't healthy." You've likely heard the phrase "healthy as a horse"… If you board your horse at a barn, own multiple horses, watch and read the news on frequent equine viral outbreaks, you might wonder how this statement ever came to be common.

Healthy as a Horse serves to reveal how to get your horse back to the vibrant health they were created and designed to experience. Packed with simple to implement steps and an age old, forgotten framework that delivers tangible results when put into practice.

If your horse experiences symptoms or has been labeled with things such as EPM, Gastric Ulcers, Aural Plaque, Heaves, Hives, Allergies, RAO, Laminitis, Insulin Resistance, PSSM, PPID, Arthritis, Wobblers, or anything else that exists on the ever expanding laundry list of horse health conditions and concerns... You're reading the right book!

On the other hand… It may be your horse is currently healthy, but you lose sleep at night or worry about that list of concerns that you just read in the paragraph above. You see and hear of horses getting sick all

1

around and you're afraid your horse is next.

You're stressing endlessly that you might be missing something or doing something wrong in your horse's care. You might feel like it's only a matter of time before the vet visits, bills, and treatments are a day to day expense that's considered normal for the responsible horse owner.

To be clear, this book isn't focused on disease. It won't help you treat any disease, prevent, or mitigate anything. Even the story I'll share about my horse's health transformation has nothing to do with a disease or illness she had or didn't have.

It has to do with HEALTH; your horse feeling better, greeting you at the gate, having the play and exuberance a horse is known for having. If that's what you're ready to focus on you're in the right place.

It's pure B.S. or in the case of this book H.S. that you as the horse owner should expect or think that your horse experiencing regular and persistent minor and major health concerns is inevitable.

If you're ready for your horse to become healthy as a horse should be… Then dive into what this book has to offer you. Don't think that your vet, trainer, farrier, or other equine professional has been taught this framework or to be honest will believe that it's true or that it will work.

I'll share more on how I came to realize firsthand that the current equine industry as a whole is running on outdated, sometimes misguided, pure misinformation that ultimately costs you a lot of money… And causes your horse a lot of needless suffering.

THAT ONE SPECIAL HORSE

Even if you have a whole herd of horses, or you've had a number of horses that have been a part of your life, truth be told, there's likely one that touched your heart and soul in such a profound way that there will simply never be another horse quite like that ONE.

For me, that horse was my first horse. Her name is Pokey, short for Pocahontas, which some sources say means "playful one", "ill-behaved child", or "spoiled child"... All to which I can happily admit has been the case for most of her life. Sadly, not all of it.

I would like to take a moment to share her story with you, because her story is what inspired what I share in this book, which has gone on to improve the health and quality of life of many horses around the world, long before this book came to be.

Her health ultimately forced me to pull off the blinders, that so many in the horse world choose to leave on. I had to let go of old traditions and false truths that had been taught to me from a very young age and likely these are the same things you've been taught and told as well.

Had it not been for this amazing horse and our painful, yet purposeful journey together, it's likely I never would have had the revelation that I was doing everything WRONG, which sucked and honestly was a tough pill to swallow... Let's be real here and admit that we horse lovers can be strong willed, independent, and not too open to "new" ways of doing things.

Before I get to Pokey's story, I'd like to shed some light on where this horse obsession started for me. Like many of us, I believe it was there at birth. It's in my bones and my DNA. I imagine it is for you as well, even if you didn't get your first horse until you were an adult, it's likely you felt drawn to them and captivated long before that time.

Surprisingly, I didn't come from a family that shared my affinity for horses. Yet, from as young as I can remember, I loved them. It became serious when I learned to read... I began studying ALL things horses. Yep complete book nerd, as I had no horses in my life at the time.

I remember receiving a horse encyclopedia as a gift and being so ecstatic to read and absorb every bit of knowledge I could. I read horse magazines and took equine focused classes offered through the Agriculture Department of our high school. From 4-H, FFA, judging competitions, internships, and more, there was never a doubt in my mind that working with horses was the future for me.

Around the age of nine or 10 was my first hands-on experience with horses (actually ponies and donkeys to be more accurate) began. I had the opportunity to volunteer at a local summer camp saddling ponies every morning. I learned a lot from the old man that ran the day camp and those feisty ponies. Even my first fall and broken bones happened there.

I don't remember much of what led up to Bobby bucking me off that morning. I do remember knowing it was a bad idea to get on him. Because it all began with the old man informing me that it was my job to stay on and show Bobby who was boss...

The pressure was on, as I climbed on Bobby with the simple task of riding him across the arena to the tie line of other ponies who were saddled and ready for a long hot day of "trail" riding around a small pasture edge with the young camp attendees.

Next thing I recall is a mouthful of dirt and mostly the sting of my pride as I heard the old man telling me to get up and get back on… Despite knowing again that it was a BAD idea, I did it anyway. I held back the tears, pushed past the fear, and got back on.

Round two, landed me on my back, and one of Bobby's hindlegs crushing down on my side. I still remember far more embarrassment and shame of coming off then I do any physical pain at the time. Needless to say, I didn't get back on Bobby that morning. I didn't go to a nurse and my mom wasn't called… In fact, she didn't know about it until months later.

We learned at a routine doctor's exam that I had broken my ribs… I knew there was a lot of swelling, bruising, and pain in the weeks after the incident, but I had kept it a secret in fear of not being able to volunteer at the day camp anymore. Luckily, by the time the truth was discovered that opportunity came and went.

But my passion and obsession for horses was still intact. So much so that I was prepared to take on an even bigger challenge than the spirited rank, rib cracking pony Bobby… It was time for me to face the infamous, horse resistant and naysaying father.

My Dad didn't and still doesn't care much for horses… But I knew that it was he and he alone that stood between me and my dream of owning my own horse. Luckily, my persistence and my father's complete lack of knowledge of my connections as a determined, horse loving girl paid off. He finally uttered the words he might still regret to this day, "I will buy you a horse, if you can find one for $100."

SOLD! You see, my best friend's parents hauled horses to slaughter at the time and when I asked if they could find me a horse for $100, they said yes. I had the pick between two perfect, beautiful weanlings. An appy my friend named Sweetheart or a bay filly she had named Pocahontas.

Well, I gave that one away already. My father's fate was sealed, he bought me my first horse… Pocahontas (nickname Pokey). We didn't have a pen or place setup to bring Pokey home at first, so she had to stay at the feedlot for a while… That's where the vet arrived to complete the vet check.

So earlier when I said perfect, beautiful weanlings, you should know that was through the eyes of a young, horse obsessed girl. Through the eyes of the vet that came to look her over, (thankfully after the purchase), he saw a malnourished, tick infested, not likely to survive weanling.

That's where it all began. Pokey was responsible for teaching me how to ride. What could have been a hot mess between her poor start, my youth and her youth - the whole green on green makes black and blue - was a blessed journey of many years of lessons, showing, trail rides, and solid investments in my lifelong passion for horses.

Fast forward through the details of those years and shortly after high school graduation, I found myself in a difficult place. You see my parents had decided to move to Alaska and having just moved out on my own, I did not have the finances to board Pokey anywhere.

I began reaching out to places I had worked and interned at, hoping to work in trade for board. I asked friends who had property. Yet, I found nothing. From a young age, I had always taken pride in being resourceful and I felt I was failing Pokey and myself miserably.

At that point, I made a decision that I still haven't 100% let go of or forgiven myself for… I sold Pokey. To be more accurate and honest, I had also managed at this young, naive time of my life to get myself in a position of needing a vehicle. So I actually traded Pokey for a truck. Admitting that still feels very gross and wrong, but it's what I did.

There is a long story and a lot that happened in the years that followed me selling Pokey, but to get on with the details of you transforming your horse's health, I'll move on. About five or six years after trading my childhood dream and best friend for a truck… I was married, owned my own home, and was looking to have a horse in my life again.

After months of frustration, searching ads, and trying horses that I didn't like, I was ready to throw in the towel. I thought maybe my time owning horses was over. Late one night I decided to search online to see what horses might be available (this was back in 2007, so it wasn't as common as it is now to search online). It was the last place I looked, my last ditch effort.

I stumbled across a website that was strictly for horse listings, I don't even remember the name of it. The only search criteria I used was my state and as I browsed through the listings, something caught my eye.

There was no picture. Very little description other than grade mare,

5

her location, that she was broke to ride, and currently bred.

So what caught my attention?

Name: Pokey.

What was certain to be a long shot, turned out to be the biggest blessing that I could've imagined. Pokey had made her way back into my life and with this magical twist of fate, I just knew everything was going to be alright. After all, what could possibly rain on this amazing parade?

WAKE UP CALL

Even after I had sold my soul and traded Pokey for a truck, I continued my pursuit of a future with horses. I had worked with local horse trainers and the local equestrian veterinary clinic, but what I had seen and experienced was definitely NOT the future I had in mind.

So I got my Equine Massage Therapist Certification and followed it with an Equine Sports Training Certification. Then put it to work at a local equine rehabilitation facility. It seemed my days were full of working with horses with aches, pains, minor health conditions, or recovering from major health conditions. Little did I realize, this was considered normal... Even by me.

When that's all you see and experience day in and day out, I suppose there isn't any other way to think. Right?

I did have an inner frustration that I couldn't get my clients' horses to a state they didn't need me... That might sound like a bad business model to hope for, but in my heart I felt horses should be healthy, overall. There simply was no evidence around me to show that as a fact.

So I went along with it, like so many other equine professionals and horse owners do. Settling for, not so healthy horses. That was until Pokey's health began to spiral out of control.

Leading up to this time, she had some concerns that had caught my attention. She was crabby, overly "mareish", she sometimes would charge me (teeth bared, ears pinned), she seemed dull, and would drag her hindlegs. She had even worn down flat spots on her hooves. I knew something was wrong.

I was giving her the best, top recommended supplements and fortified grains. I had vets, chiropractors, and other body workers assess her and they found nothing. They told me she was just a grumpy, lazy mare.

So I just kept doing what everyone else was doing (what the experts told me)... Even though in my heart I knew something was wrong. Then in the fall of 2011, Pokey lost control of her hindquarters. She had to lean on fences and panels to stay upright.

I was shocked, heartbroken, and devastated. Again I went to the vets, my mentors and contacts... One vet said EPM, another said Cushings, and the third said possible brain tumor. I was frustrated, confused, and angry; adding to the emotions I was already feeling.

Why couldn't anyone get on the same page? How did this happen? What did I miss?

I had racked up thousands of dollars in vet bills and specialist fees and the ONLY thing they could all agree on was that putting Pokey down was my best and only option.

At that time, she was around 20 or 21 years old. What infuriated me further was the professionals and vets made it seem like it was perfectly normal and to be expected for horses to experience a major and often rapid decline of health around this age...

Seriously?!?

This turn of events and experience with Pokey almost drove me out of the horse industry completely. As a professional and a horse owner. I simply could not tolerate that out of all the years of "top of the line" feeds, supplements, and therapies this is the fate that horses had to look forward to.

Pokey wasn't even a performance horse or athlete. I couldn't imagine if this was "normal" for a recreational horse like her... What did the industry standard say was status quo for them?

BLINDERS OFF AND DUKES UP

Maybe it was because I had already lost Pokey once in my life, that I wasn't willing to do it again... I don't know why I didn't accept the fate that all the experts, peers, and mentors of mine tried to sell me. Even most of my friends thought I was being irrational and crazy for keeping Pokey alive.

Something in me knew she wasn't ready to leave this earth. She wasn't done. It was also at this point that I started to see the lies or ignorance we had been sold as both horse owners and equine professionals.

I thought about horses out in the wild and how although some die at a young age, many of them live for years beyond our pampered domestic horses. The Mustangs live in harsh and unforgiving conditions. Yet, overall, if you look at their health, they are... Quite healthy.

In fact, they are so healthy and thrive so well, here in the US, our government has taken to rounding them up and other drastic measures to control their populations. The details on this would be a whole other book... And please don't believe the stories that illness and starvation is the mission behind these actions. Like most things, it's greed, money, and power.

Mustangs thrive in health, yet with all the scientifically complete nutrition, vaccinations, chemical deworming routines, traditional metal shoes to protect the horse's hooves, and all the highly praised procedures and medications... The domestic horse faces far more illness, disease, lameness, and problems than those in the wild.

This awareness was something that came later in my journey of improving my horse's health and quality of life.

At my time of desperation, I first looked at natural remedies to get her condition to an improved state. I successfully utilized essential oils and saw dramatic improvements, but I knew that Pokey didn't get to this state of disease overnight.

Although it seemed to have appeared suddenly, I thought back to her behavior changes and subtle things I had seen over the last few years that everyone told me was normal. I understood that within the care routine and lifestyle there must have been things I did that "fed" this problem.

Knowing that the very things I had done day in and day out, day after day, month after month were what everyone else was doing too, I began to connect the dots that there was more to understand and change than simply adding the essential oils to Pokey's care.

At the time of writing this book, Pokey is still here with me now. She's over 30 years old and I cherish every day I've been blessed to have her in my life. Once I began to see drastic improvements in Pokey's health, I began suggesting the same changes for my clients. Their horse's experienced positive results as well and my lifelong journey into mastering health and getting horse's looking and feeling their best as nature intended, had officially begun.

A few years into my new found path, I discovered the concept of Naturopathy… I completed a practitioner program offered through the American Council of Animal Naturopathy. It simply validated that what I was doing was a "real" thing. Everything they taught aligned with what I was doing.

Inside this book are the steps I take with my personal horses. They are what I share with my clients, for them to explore and decide to implement for their horses. I'm a coach and educator. I'm not a licensed veterinarian or medical professional, nor do I have any desire to be one or pretend that I am one.

What I teach and share is not medical advice and I don't diagnose, treat, cure, or mitigate a disease or illness. What I did for my horse didn't "cure" anything.

My focus and what I teach is health, not disease. Lifestyle, nutrition, and care. So if you're looking to learn more about health, let's get started.

PART ONE

Foundation

You only get one chance to live with and experience your horse. Even if you have a whole herd of them, your time to love, cherish, enjoy, and care for each unique, individual horse is right now.

And there is no one that knows how to care for your horse better than you do, even if you're not feeling so confident about it at this moment.

It's likely that you've been wanting to provide more natural care for your horse for awhile now...

You feel the tug and deep knowledge that there are better ways to keep, feed, and be with your horse.

In fact, the consequences if you don't make the changes you innately know need to be made are inevitable, your horse might already be experiencing them now, from a long list of health conditions.

Or it could be that you see it in the lackluster, suffering horses all around you and you don't want that life for your horse....

The amazing thing is, you can empower yourself now and change the path for your horse if you want to.

Versus wait until it's too late and live with the regret of what you could've or should've done while you had the chance.

Ultimately, the decision is up to you...

But where do you need to start and what do you need to do?

First and foremost, you must establish a FOUNDATION of health for your horse. Just like your home needs solid ground to stand on, so does your horse's health.

Part 1 of this book will walk you through the lifestyle, nutrition, and digestive health basics your horse needs to maintain or recover health. Don't be fooled into thinking you have been taught this information before or that your equine professional has the answers you need.

Let's get started on the foundation to your horse's health!

CHAPTER ONE

The Elephant in the Horse Industry

LET'S TALK ABOUT IT

The elephant in the horse industry, that no one wants to talk about, is the alarming amount of horse waste, neglect, and disregard of preserving or honoring the horse's dignity… And it's happening all the time.

I experienced this when I went to work for a few world class trainers in my area. I recall one internship I did through high school. I wasn't paid, it was to gain experience in the field and explore what I wanted to do for a living. What I saw happen to the horses there broke my heart. Every day I had to go there, I would get physically sick to my stomach with angst and dread. I often spent hours crying when I got home… After a full semester of this, I knew I didn't want to be a horse trainer if that's what it entailed.

Now to clarify, I understand that not all trainers are this way. But we can't deny that this is happening on a massive scale across the industry. There is a professional training facility near me that has a pasture of broad mares, many of which are lame. One close look will reveal they no longer receive regular hoof care. Yet the owners and trainers make thousands and hundreds of thousands of dollars from the offspring of these horses.

After seeing what was happening to these horses, I decided the best place for me to be would be to help these horses with their health and injuries... So I decided to intern at a local equine veterinary clinic.

Much to my dismay, things didn't look any brighter there. It seemed once horses started coming into the clinic, one of two things happened...

1. They repeatedly continued to need care, treatment, medication, and procedures (meaning health was never fully restored.)
2. They were put down.

Please don't think I'm being pessimistic here, nor am I looking to say that the veterinary field is bad or doing this intentionally, it's simply an observation made by someone who wanted to improve the quality of life and health of horses and could find no evidence that it was going to happen in this profession.

Could this be connected to the high amount of suicide rates among veterinarians?

An article published by Time Magazine, September 2019, titled 'Veterinarians Face Unique Issues That Make Suicide One of the Profession's Big Worries', stated:

"The job challenges that more than 70,000 veterinarians in the U.S. face have led to disproportionately high suicide rates, according to the U.S. Centers for Disease Control and Prevention (CDC). Nearly 400 veterinarians died by suicide between 1979 and 2015, according to a CDC study published in January that analyzed more than 11,000 veterinarian death records in that timeframe. The study also found that female veterinarians are up to 3.5 times more likely to kill themselves than members of the general population. "It really can be classified as an epidemic in my profession," says McCauley, who is now 36 and working for a trade association in Washington, D.C."

These are truths that no one wants to acknowledge, but that doesn't mean they aren't there... The number of illnesses, diseases, and viral infections are on the rise. Yet people talk about the breakthroughs in medicine that are making horses healthier and helping them live longer.

It's not in my nature to rock the boat, but I'm willing to shine light and empower people to look deeper into what's real and what's being swept under the rug.

But before you go blaming, pointing fingers, getting angry, or shouting from the rooftops, here's the most important thing to know: You can change this current reality. Without becoming an activist, without riots, and anything disrupting your current life.

In fact, the steps shared in this book are designed to help you be the very change the industry needs… Even better news, in the process, you'll likely save time and money; creating the space for you to have more enjoyment and fulfillment in owning your horse.

But anytime you're reading this book and implementing one of the steps and a friend, peer, an equine professional, or vet chimes in about how crazy you are and how nuts I must be to think what I'm sharing will work… Know that they still have their blinders on.

Have compassion and understanding for where they are. No need to try to "fix" or change their views. Just keep empowering yourself, learning, and growing.

Sooner or later, your horse's radiant health and your care routine will serve as an example that others will be drawn to learn more about and if they aren't… No big deal. You've done all you need to do by transforming the health and life of the horse or herd you're responsible for caring for. That alone makes a difference, and will have a positive impact.

WHAT IS HEALTH?

Health encompasses the physical, mental, and emotional aspects of the horse. Health is a pursuit. A constant ebb and flow of substances and forces; of the physical and the energetic vibrations within the body. Although there is never a perfect balance within the body, health is present when the body's systems and energies are harmonizing and synchronizing together.

The world we live in has become inundated with hazards and disruptions that we must seek to consistently and persistently offset. Few will take this task on fully, whether for their personal health or that of their horse…

The real reason is often hidden in a blind-spot and disguised by comforting excuses like not having enough time, money, resources, or simply life getting in the way. The reality is it's the refusal of releasing control that prevents us from taking responsibility for one's health. Combine that with the ease and convenience of the current trends of the traditional health care system that sells and promises results and health from procedures, medications, and human ingenuity.

Don't be fooled, nature does not yield to our illusions. Disease and illness is a signal from the body of disharmony and imbalance. No pill, procedure, or medication will get to the root cause of the disruption.

It might serve as a temporary distraction or relief of the symptoms or sounding alarm, but I assure you that is all. Modern medicine serves an important role in health care, especially during times of trauma, emergency, or injury.

Yet, what commonly happens is your horse gets caught up in a system of managing disease and masking disruptions that will empty your pocketbook and lead to prolonged suffering for your horse. When your horse shows signs of a health condition, whether it be hives, labored breathing, or sudden weight loss, it can appear that the problem came on suddenly. This is only because the horse industry as a whole has overlooked the subtle signs that the horse's body gave leading to the bigger problem.

Think for a minute about the boiling frog analogy… You know the one, where the pot of water starts at lukewarm and comfortable for the frog, then ever so slowly the heat is increased to the point of boiling. The frog, comfortable and unaware of the slowly rising temperatures remains until it's too late to jump.

For your horse, it could have started with a slight behavior change, or decrease in performance; maybe less brightness in the eyes, dryness in the coat, stiffness or less mobility in their neck, shoulder, or stifles.

These slight shifts are often addressed by adding a supplement or fancy therapy treatment that unknowingly serves as a mask to the cause and like the gradual warming of the water for the frog, your horse's body "turns up the heat" with more and more signals that we often see as unrelated. Continuing the masking process until the "water boils", which for your horse means a major health condition suddenly appears. It could look like colic, gastric ulcers, laminitis, arthritis, metabolic conditions, or a laundry list of other concerns.

The good news is you can empower yourself to see and take action on the subtle signs. You've got the right resource in your hands to help you do just that. Even if your horse is experiencing more chronic or problematic conditions, the principles shared in this book will serve you in giving your horse's body what it needs to regain balance. Because ultimately, that's what health is… Homeostasis and balance.

When health is lost and disease sets in, don't fall into the trap of honing in on the disease. This will simply further offset and wreak havoc on the systems of the body, ensuring that homeostasis will NOT be restored.

Develop the core belief and understanding that disease is often the result of many previous symptoms and actions of the body being suppressed or treated versus listening to and properly resolving the subtle signs on the onset.

Often times in life, it's best to go against the flow. Do the opposite of what you see others doing. Your horse's health is no different! If you want a thriving, vibrant horse, you need to do what most are simply not open and willing to do.

You must master and anchor in on health. Keep in mind that mastery requires patience, which most people choose not to develop. They fall for quick fixes and bandaid approaches that will compound the negative effects in the future.

Know that putting what this book teaches into action often feels counterintuitive at first. It also is a sharp contrast to what everyone in the industry has done, at least for many years. So resistance from your peers, mentors, and even the professionals you work with is likely and to be expected.

THE 8 LAWS OF HEALTH

"The fundamental principles of Nature Cure philosophy, which radically differ from allopathic theory and practice, and which are destined to revolutionize the chaotic teachings of the old schools and to establish in their place an exact science of medicine, are the following: Every acute disease is the result of a purifying, healing effort of Nature." ~ Dr. Henry Lindlahr

The first step to transforming your horse's health is to align their lifestyle and care to what is referred to as the 8 Laws of Health. While I'm not sure where these laws originated, I was first introduced to them when I completed the certification program at the American Council of Animal Naturopathy.

When I saw these laws laid out, I knew they were true laws and principles that would generate health, because it was what I had done to help my mare Pokey and for my clients that were experiencing the best results, they had also implemented these changes.

Health is found and maintained through respecting and following these 8 Laws of Health:

1. Nutrition - We will cover this topic extensively in Chapter 2 as it's likely one of the BIGGEST concerns to your horse's health right now… The current trends and market is full of synthetic and chemical laden junk food that's promoted by vets, trainers, farriers, and even nutritionists. Yet, it's like choosing to feed health concerns one scoop or bucket at a time. EVERYDAY! Each species is designed to eat certain foods to maintain optimal health. We'll dive into what your horse is created and designed to eat in the next chapter.

2. Exercise - A body in motion tends to stay in motion. Your horse is designed to move daily to keep the systems of the body in flow and harmony. What's common for domesticated horses is to get far too little exercise, like recreational horses that don't get ridden often and are kept in stalls or small paddocks. The flip side is the athlete and performance horse, that often gets more strenuous exercise than the body should endure for long periods of time. As a horse keeper and caregiver, it's your responsibility and part of your horse's health maintenance plan to ensure you are providing balance and moderation in this area.

3. Water - Your horse's body is mostly comprised of water, so ensuring that your horse has adequate hydration and fresh water available at all times is crucial to health. In Chapter 3, we'll explore what you need to know about your horse's digestive system and you'll gain an understanding of why impaction and blockage is common in horses, especially when they aren't properly hydrated.

Although this appears to be common sense, there are factors within this law that are often overlooked. First, understanding there are negative impacts that the chemicals in the water have on your horse. Second, raising your awareness to any further action you might need to take to reduce those chemicals. These are simple ways to improve wellbeing that people don't think about for their horse.

Herbicides, pesticides, and other agricultural chemicals can pollute the irrigation water you might use to water your horse. Treated tap water or well water can contain high amounts of chlorine and fluoride. Utilizing affordable filter options available on the market that contain eco-friendly coconut carbon and high purity copper-zinc granules can be an easy way to not only filter impurities that are detrimental to your horse's health, some horses will increase their water consumption when these impurities are removed!

I experienced this firsthand with one of my personal horses, Peppy. Shortly after purchasing him, he had a severe impaction colic. The vets were not optimistic he would survive… Thankfully, my prompt action to get him medical attention and several days of intravenous fluids and intensive care, he did. It was a long road to full recovery, but during that recovery and with closer observation of his hydration, it became clear that he was not voluntarily drinking the quantities of water that he should. I tried supplements and electrolytes, but I wasn't content with using them long-term. He would visit the trough often during the day, but not always drink. He would sniff and splash the water around and leave.

A friend of mine had recently talked to me about a filter offered from a company called Horse Hydrator. It was a small, affordable filter I attached to the end of the hose. Within the first day of utilizing this filter, Peppy had increased his drinking substantially.

I don't have an exact measurement as multiple horses drank from the trough; it was through observing his visits to the trough and the frequency that he would drink while at the trough. I saw improvements in his overall health, due to the increased hydration as well. He was more fluid in his movement, his skin wasn't as dry, and much to my relief, his poops were softer, more moist, and less compact.

4. Sun - Your horse receiving adequate sunlight is important to their health. The horse will self regulate when given the ability to do so. Now, before you get annoyed or maybe giggle at the simplicity of these 8 Laws of Health, understand that major health conditions are often the result of repeated small violations of these laws.

Although it seems again like common sense that a horse needs sunlight, some facilities aren't designed with long enough turnouts for horses that otherwise will spend their day inside a covered stall. I encourage you to NOT take these things lightly. Allow yourself the willingness and openness to really ask and rate your horse's lifestyle with each law shared.

5. Moderation - All things should be applied and offered in moderation. Because too much or too little of anything is a concern. This is a law that as humans, I believe generally is a struggle. If you look at society as a whole, we are experts of being excessive in many ways. Even those whose goal is to use only the essentials or the minimalists often take it to an extreme. Can you relate or see it too? This concept of temperance ties into the other laws, as often any imbalance with nutrition, exercise, water, sun, air, rest, or trust requires practicing moderation to bring balance.

6. Air - The biggest factor for air is quality. In our domesticated environments, musky barns that possibly harbor mold and other pathogens of concern, or densely populated areas with heavy air pollution, can violate this law and drastically increase risks of respiratory issues. Even in rural areas with heavy agriculture, if chemical sprays are frequently utilized for crops, this is a factor to consider.

7. Rest - Stress can hinder health and raise the risk of illness and even result in behavioral issues. Adequate rest and sleep are essential to maintaining health. This law often serves with exercise hand in hand. If rest is out of balance, it's likely that exercise is as well, and the other way around. Performance horses can suffer from not enough rest, while the recreational horse can experience too much rest.

8. Trust - Horses are living creatures... There is their emotion and free will to consider. Trust and bond between horse and rider is a crucial part of health that many wish to overlook or avoid... There is also an element of trust and understanding in these laws required by you as the horse owner. Because society has ventured so far from nature they will challenge your decisions and beliefs in these laws.

The 8 Laws of Health show that health is not left to chance or luck, but is something that can be built, supported, and even repaired when lost. Abiding by these laws will give horses the foundation of health they would have naturally pursued in the wild.

When laws are broken, there are consequences. Human-made or composed laws might require you to be "caught", although this may not always happen. But nature's laws have real consequences that cannot be avoided. For example, think of the law of gravity.

If you're violating or out of balance with these laws, your horse will likely experience subtle consequences first, like decreased energy, disruption to blood or lymphatic flow, and endocrine imbalance - all which will later result in creating a cycle of dysfunction. Other factors include accumulation of morbid waste and toxins, increased inflammation, oxidative stress, and build up of the perfect environment for pathogens and "bad" bacteria, fungus, and viruses to flourish.

Regardless of what you implement in your horse's lifestyle, you must ensure that you have aligned their care as closely as humanly possible to these 8 Laws of Health before you do anything else.

Every supplement, feed, vaccine, chemical, medication, and so on that violates these laws WILL impact the health and wellness of your horse. Yes, some things are beyond your ability to change… That's why taking responsibility for what you can is imperative for the long-term health of your horse.

CHOOSING WHICH YOU WANT TO MAGNIFY

You've likely heard the saying that what you focus on magnifies… Well it's another concept that applies to your horse's health! Every day, think of it like you're walking around with a big magnifying glass and you choose what you get to hold over.

My question to you is "Do you wish to magnify health or problems?" Of course no one knowingly wants to magnify their horse's problems and yet, that's what so many people, I would say a MAJORITY of horse owners, are currently doing!

If your current care routine consists of heavily processed and synthetic feeds and supplements, antibiotics, rounds of medications, chemical dewormers, and frequent vaccinations, your horse is likely experiencing repeated minor health concerns because without realizing it, you're holding your magnifying glass over "problems". So naturally, you will get more and more of them.

Meanwhile, if you're focused on clean, wholefood based, species-specific nutrition, supporting a healthy microbiome with prebiotics, probiotics, digestive enzymes, using natural remedies like herbs, essential oils, and homeopathy to regularly promote health, you're focusing on "health". And for the times you need to utilize disruptive medications, treatments, or vaccines, you have a plan in place to support the body through cleansing and restoration. Your magnifying glass is magnifying health and it likely appears that your horse and herd experiences far less health concerns than many of the horses around you.

Now, if you're wanting to change where your magnifying glass is hovering, no worries, just keep reading. I will keep shining the light on the myths and misunderstandings that have led your horse to a place of increased risk of illness and disease.

For many of you, your horse is past increased risk and in a state of disease, like my mare Pokey was. I know what that frustrating, confusing path is like. But I also know that removing the blinders isn't easy. If you're like me, some of the things I question and push back on in this book are going to go against things you've likely been taught from a VERY young age! Or whatever age you began learning about horses.

These are things that well respected people and experts have taught you, that I'm going to ask you to question… Back when I first began this journey, it helped me to remind myself that people can only share from what they know, have been taught, or personally experienced.

I struggled with a lot of anger as I worked to regain my horse's health. Things I had spent time and hard earned money on, I later discovered contributed to my horse being sick. To make that experience worse, when I shared what I knew with my mentors and teachers, they told me I was wrong and crazy; even after I was able to support my mare back to a balanced state of health!

Taking a stand for my horse's health cost me friends and in some circles, respect and reputation. Yet, what I've since gained in return is far beyond any of those initial costs. The good news is that I've been in the trenches long enough that we've built communities of horse owners that stand for their horse's health and support each other.

So if as you begin implementing the changes shared in this book you feel stuck or alone, be sure to check out our website for details on connecting to our community. You're not alone and we're here to help.

ILLNESS AND DISEASE HAVE A CLEAR PROCESS

Did you know that your horse's body has a process in which it maintains health? I first learned about this when researching and improving my own personal health. Inside the book '*The Battle for Health Is Over pH: Life and Death Hangs in the Balance*' by Gary Tunsky, these steps are walked through extensively.

I want to simply raise your awareness and introduce the steps of this process to you. As your horse's body functions day to day, it completes the following processes to maintain health: clearing waste, buffering acids, and cleansing toxins.

First, the body increases oxygen within the cells, because waste needs to bind with oxygen to leave the body. Next, the body will begin to utilize amino acid reserves, which will be eliminated via the kidneys, urinary tract, and/or sweating.

If additional waste, toxins, and build up needs cleansed, the body moves on to the high pH bodily fluids, including saliva and the lymphatic system before continuing on and pulling electrolytes from bones, teeth, and muscles. Think of horses with mineral deficiency or imbalances. When more support is still required, the body will filter through the elimination routes. This can look like respiratory conditions, skin irritation, allergies, or urinary tract issues.

We are only on the beginning steps of the process. The body is sending messages that it needs support for these cleansing and health maintaining systems. Instead, what commonly happens is the signals are suppressed or treated with acidic, toxic, or chemical-based products, medications, and treatments that only further insult this process and drive the imbalance to the next two steps, which are "disease states" of the process. These are more chronic and severe concerns.

If the body is not supported in the beginning steps, the body will begin pushing excess acids to the horse's outer extremities. This is the body's attempt to protect vital organs. The body will now store and push remaining toxins and acids that failed to be neutralized in the previous stages to the outer less "vital" parts of the body. For example, the hooves or joints, leading to degenerative diseases, metabolic concerns, and so on.

Still left unsupported, you've likely guessed or naturally know what's next... The body will be forced to push excess acids into the blood and vital organ systems. When your horse is presenting chronic and major health problems, this is the phase your horse's body is in... The body is simply overloaded with systemic waste. The cells are in a state of dysfunction and toxins are abundant and stagnant.

Once you understand this process, you can start to see there is a CLEAR path to health, which should excite you! As a horse owner, you now are empowered to support your horse's body with the process that balances the state of health or disease.

This doesn't guarantee that the cellular health can be fully restored, nor does it mean your horse's state of illness or disease will be reversed, but it does give you a tool kit and action steps to not sit idly by, clueless of how you can help.

That is how many horse owners feel when they contact me. It was definitely how I felt when my mare's health spiraled out of control. Taking the actions shared in this book will serve you in supporting this process in maintaining health. If your horse is currently experiencing health concerns, know that you can use this information to gain a clear understanding of where your horse's body is currently at, so you can effectively and efficiently do what's possible to facilitate a space for recovery and balance.

SUMMARY & ACTION STEPS

Action Step 1 - The best place to start is with the 8 Laws of Health. We have a downloadable worksheet you can use at **www. equineessentialwellness.com/bookbonus**. Begin by rating your horse's current lifestyle based on each of the 8 Laws of Health.

Use a rating scale of 1 being needs the most improvement and 10 being the closest to your horse's design as humanly possible.

Don't make this complicated and simply go with the first number that comes to mind. Simply ask yourself, "On a scale of 1 to 10, I would rate my horse's nutrition as ___." Do this for each law.

You'll want to keep these answers and for now, keep moving forward. As you dive into the next chapters, your view on some of the laws might change as new information is revealed.

Action Step 2 - Using the process that your horse's body goes through to maintain health, which state would you say that your horse is currently in:

• Health - no visible or known signs of health concern.

• Risk - has visible signs via the elimination routes - respiratory, skin irritation, allergies, hoof condition, coat and hair changes, or slight behavioral changes.

• Disease - has visible and possibly now medically diagnosed symptoms and conditions that are affecting vital organs, joints, connective tissue, and more.

This exercise is to gain awareness of where your horse is. Don't feel discouraged or fearful. You've done great so far. Keep up the amazing work and let's move on to the transformation you're looking for!

CHAPTER TWO

The Best Nutrition for Your Horse

THE INFAMOUS COMPLETE AND BALANCED NUTRITION

In Chapter 1, we unpacked the harsh reality that many people won't choose to take responsibility for health and that the hidden reason is they refuse to release the illusion of control. I know that's not the case for you, because you're still reading...

Many chapters of this book cover topics that are prime examples of the illusions of control in full swing. I'm not sure if there's a more prime example of this than your horse's nutrition.

Take a moment and think about your special horse, even if you have a herd of horses. Raise your awareness and attention to one of them right now. Think of the precious moments and memories you have with that horse. How would it feel to be able to create space for more of those moments. Quality of time and life with that horse?

From what I've experienced with my personal horses and those of the clients I've worked with, this is definitely possible and cleaning your horse's nutrition is crucial to this goal and intention.

Before we dive into equine nutrition, I want to clarify that not all horses need supplementation beyond their basic hay or forage. Ultimately, the best source of nutrition for your horse is fibrous dense forage or good quality hay. For many recreational horses, this will be adequate nutrition for their needs.

There are times because of performance, training, or increased stress or risk that a horse needs and benefits from supplementing nutrition. Most people who seek to work with me are already supplementing their horse for a specific reason, or have a focused intention as to why they feel their horse needs supplementation.

Providing the best care that you can for your horse, I know is your primary goal. None of us knowingly feed or use products and supplements that hinder our horse's health. Sadly, our horse's food has become overly processed and full of cheap fillers, toxic chemicals, and inflammation-promoting synthetics. I often use the analogy of a cupcake with a vitamin popped in the center... That's what many of the feeds on the market are like for your horse.

Making matters worse, the vitamins added are mostly lab created and the body doesn't utilize or recognize the nutrition; meaning it goes in one end and out the other, or will store in the body causing inflammation and health concern.

Remember the rising number of concerns like gastric ulcers, insulin resistance, equine metabolic disease, laminitis, founder, Cushings, and so on that we talked about in Chapter 1? It's a clear indication that we are missing the mark with all the scientifically proven and complete nutrition and our current care routines.

What will it mean for your horse if you don't clean their nutrition and get their health in balance? I discovered what happens the hard way, when my mare's health "suddenly" spiraled out of control. I mentioned I utilized essential oils and other natural remedies that I know supported her health and journey back to balance, but changing her nutrition was the pivotal change that created the space and possibility for her body to properly utilize those remedies.

If you own a diesel truck, you don't fuel it up with gas, even if an "expert" told you to. You would disregard their recommendation regardless if others all around you listened. Unlike your car or truck, that would have rapid malfunctions and breakdowns if you put in the wrong fuel, your horse's body can adapt for long periods of time. When their body begins to show the dysfunctions and concerns you've been feeding the wrong fuel for so long, often you don't even connect that's part of the problem.

Furthermore, everyone around you is feeding the same thing. So why would you question anything at all? Yet, what you fail to realize is most of their horses are also having the SAME or SIMILAR list of concerns. This was my biggest "ah ha" moment when I was first looking for solutions for my mare Pokey.

You might have flipped through the pages of this book and wondered "How can this book talk about nutrition without a bunch of graphs, ratios, and complicated charts?"

Let me be real with you, you won't find any cookie cutter, scientifically proven, ratio and percentage balanced looks into equine nutrition inside this book. I have attended courses that teach this method, but it is not what I utilize day to day in my work since 2011, when my mare became ill...

Therefore, I choose to share with you what I have seen that produces results for my personal horses and those of my clients. Years of frustration with the traditional method, is what led me to what I am sharing with you now.

Like all the other care I provide for my horses, it's now focused on each horse as a unique individual, not some blanket approach that should work for all horses. Yes, we'll share simple core fundamentals and provide a road map of what you want to look for, but "the control it all", analyze every flake of hay, or spreadsheet every vitamin and mineral that enters your horse's body approach that is becoming more and more popular, won't be shared here.

Remember how I said, look at what everyone else is doing, and do the opposite… That's what you'll always see in this book and any of the resources I offer.

SPOTTING SYNTHETICS

The first thing I want to empower you to do with your horse's nutrition is spot the synthetics, fillers, and additives in an ingredient list. Now, I'm not saying that you should never feed or utilize synthetics, but going back to the 8 Laws of Health of Chapter 1… It needs to be in moderation when you do.

Most fortified and cereal grains on the market resemble that cupcake with a synthetic vitamin in the middle and when fed day after day, it will increase your horse's risk of health concerns. For example ingredient lists be sure to head over to **www.equineessentialwellness.com/bookbonus**.

What you'll need to complete this exercise is the ingredient lists from ALL your horse's feeds and supplements. Even if you believe you're feeding a plain hay pellet or your feed is recommended by your trainer, vet, or farrier, you will want to review each of the ingredient lists.

In fact, I encourage you to know the ingredients of every product you put on and in your horse. It might feel tedious, but there are often health damaging ingredients in the products on the shelves today and unless you raise your awareness, you're paying these companies to put your horse at risk. Ultimately, it's your responsibility as the horse keeper to be aware and mindful of the decisions you're making in the day to day care of your horse.

Whether you can tear an ingredient list paper from a bag or use your phone to get a picture off the bag or bucket, it's best to use the ingredient list directly off the supplement versus the company's website. Some websites aren't updated regularly and might only share the active ingredients. Even on the feeds I love and use now, I consistently review the ingredient lists for changes.

Let's clear up a few terms commonly used around your horse's care products:

- **Natural** - existing in or caused by nature; not made or caused by humankind.
- **Organic** - relating to or derived from living matter.
- **Synthetic** - (of a substance) made by chemical synthesis, especially to imitate a natural product.

What is important to note is that labeling has twisted and contorted these words. Companies can label a product as natural even if it's made mostly of synthetic ingredients.

"Unfortunately, vitamins can be labeled as natural if they contain as little as 10% of the natural form of the vitamin. This means that your "natural" vitamin could contain 90% of synthetically produced chemicals! B-Vitamins and Vitamin C are also usually synthetically produced." ~ Dr. Edward Group DC, NP, DACBN, DCBCN, DABFM

Animal products have less regulation or requirements for what must be listed on the label. Another thing to watch for is that manufacturers can also "hide" ingredients inside their proprietary blend.

Your goal is to increase the amount of whole food, species-specific ingredients contained in the feeds and supplements you choose to utilize as opposed to having a long list of synthetic, filler, or additive ingredients that your horse's body must filter, process, and cleanse before it can utilize the nutrients within.

Natural nutrients are obtained from whole food sources in the diet, and synthetic nutrients are typically made artificially, through an industrial process. It's important to note that the production process of synthetic nutrients is not the same, nor does it compare to the way plants and animals create them. So despite having a similar makeup, your horse's body will likely respond differently to synthetics.

It's often unexplored how well the horse's body absorbs and utilizes synthetic nutrition. Your horse would not naturally intake singled out nutrients… Instead, they would consume a whole range of vitamins, minerals, cofactors and enzymes that allow for optimal use by their body. This combined with the fact that the body may not recognize synthetic nutrients only adds to the health risk and concern of relying too much on synthetic ingredients.

When reviewing the ingredient list of your horse's grains and supplements, watch out for the following:

- Ingredients that end in "ate"
- Ingredients that end in "ide"
- Ingredients listed as a "dl-" form
- Ingredients listed as vitamins on the ingredient list (ex. Vitamin C)

You might wonder how a vitamin listed on the ingredient list would be synthetic… If it's listed on the ingredient list it was added in a synthetic form versus gaining it from a whole food source. There are some vitamins that can only be supplemented synthetically, as its formed during a chemical reaction or synthesis within the body. But the goal with my horses and what I encourage is to support the body's natural production of the vitamin or feeding a whole food option known for its high content of that vitamin wherever possible.

The goal of sharing this information isn't to vilify certain ingredients, or even synthetics for that matter. But the current trends, to lean on synthetics, do have a negative impact on health. Now that you've been empowered to spot them, you as the horse owner can decide if feeding 10, 20, 30, or more synthetic ingredients day after day is what you choose to do.

Once you've identified the synthetics, if you really wish to keep your horse on a product that contains quite a few, you might search the internet for information on each of the synthetics listed. This will give you a broader understanding of why it was included and additional facts like cautions, lack of digestibility, and so on.

My current care routine contains very few (often less than 10 synthetic or non whole food ingredients). Most of the clients and students that report the most dramatic health improvement in their horse have also followed these steps to not have synthetics in their horse's feed or supplements.

An example of a time I often make an exception is something like a stabilized rice bran meal. This is a common option I like to utilize if I have a horse that has dry sounding, cracking joints or that needs to gain weight through an increased fat intake.

Even the cleanest stabilized rice bran ingredient list is going to contain a preservative like Calcium Carbonate. Again, this information serves to empower you as you make decisions in your horse's care. I still have students and clients who feed high amounts of synthetics. But I openly express my experience has been that they will not receive the same results as those clients open to making more natural changes. Because over time, that has been proven to be the case.

NUTRITION BASICS TO KEEP IN MIND

The goal of this chapter isn't to have you studying for hours or to give you a degree in equine nutrition, it's to empower you with the basics of what your horse needs to thrive naturally.

Breaking down and understanding the different nutrients that horses need and can digest will give insight into how to provide the horse with a proper diet. We will begin with carbohydrates.

For a general understanding, horses digest two broad and different groups of carbohydrates.

Glucose units called beta bonds cannot be properly broken down by digestive enzymes. Instead, these resistant starches and fiber will pass to the large intestine where the microbial fermentation will aid in digesting and breaking down for the nutrients to be utilized by the body. Glucose units called alpha bonds can be broken down via enzymatic digestion and will be processed and utilized by the small intestine.

Many nutritional fibers are classified as carbohydrates, although some are not (such as lignin). Although some people may think of fiber as dietary "filler", given the fact that the horse's digestive tract is designed to process high levels of fiber, it is an extremely important carbohydrate in equine nutrition. Furthermore, all herbivores need a certain amount of non digestible fiber for gastrointestinal health and function.

Carbohydrates are a primary source of energy for the horse. Their digestive system is designed by nature to digest high levels of fiber. So it is important to understand that fiber for a horse is not a dietary filler but actually a species-specific necessity. Quality and species appropriate fiber is also something to gain awareness of as many commercial, processed grains will use cheap and poor quality fiber fillers and claim they are good for the horse.

All carbohydrates are saccharides. What we know as sugars in a horse's diet consists of monosaccharides and disaccharides. Monosaccharides are referred to as the building blocks of energy and nucleic acids; they are also the simplest of carbohydrates. Glucose, fructose, galactose, mannose, arabinose, and xylose are all monosaccharides that are important to equine nutrition. Moving on to disaccharides that are important to the horse include lactose and maltose.

Oligosaccharides are believed by some to be simple sugars, while others prefer to see them as polysaccharides. The purpose and importance of at least some oligosaccharides may be that of a "prebiotic". Prebiotics can be defined as non-digestible food components that can have beneficial effects on the host by selectively stimulating certain bacteria. Some common and important oligosaccharides for horses can be raffinose, stachyose, maltotriosem fructooligosaccharide.

There are two main categories of vitamins to consider when we investigate equine nutrition:

- Fat Soluble - Vitamins A, D, E, and K
- Water Soluble - Vitamins B and C

We'll discuss more about storage, benefits and sources of each of the vitamins listed above in hopes of helping you gain a good foundation in understanding the nutritional needs of your horse.

Vitamin A - is an essential key nutrient for horses and is heavily studied and commonly added or included in many equine supplements and grain options. Vitamin A supports vision, specifically night vision, immune function, reproduction, fertility, fetus growth, red blood cell production, and more.

This list helps us understand the popularity and need of Vitamin A, but what else should we know about it?

A horse's body will naturally convert Vitamin A from beta-carotene in plants. Fresh forage that is not in a state of dormancy will contain higher amounts of beta-carotene, and therefore allow for the horse to produce or convert more Vitamin A.

Vitamin A is stored in the liver and can be utilized and stored upwards of six months at a time. This could be seen as a way for the horse to preserve and thrive during seasons that forage would be less abundant and dormant.

Since horses convert this vitamin from the consumption of beta-carotene, it seems strange that you will see Vitamin A listed on ingredient lists of supplements… That is due to the fact that supplemental forms of beta-carotene seem to limit the ability and efficiency of conversion, which then leads to the inclusion and use of stabilized or synthetic forms of Vitamin A like retinyl palmitate or retinyl acetate.

By reviewing the list of systems that Vitamin A supports the health of, you can also understand what the signs of deficiency might be: night blindness, eye irritation and concern, compromised immunity, and other concerns. What is interesting is the signs of toxicity and buildup are not vastly different.

Due to the storage in the liver, excessive Vitamin A could result in symptoms including things such as skin irritation, flaking or itching, bone disorders, birth defects in foals, depression, loss of hair, and even possible death.

As mentioned before, fresh forage is a great source for the horse to convert Vitamin A naturally. Alfalfa is often higher in beta-carotene than grass. For horses that do not graze on live grasses, it is important to be aware of the storage time of hay. Over time, the efficiency of the beta-carotene conversion to Vitamin A decreases and in such cases, supplementation could be beneficial to maintain the health of the horse. Dandelion leaves, oregano, and carrots are high in beta-carotene for natural whole food supplemental options to be considered in moderation.

Vitamin B Complex - Although gastrointestinal tract health is crucial for all vitamin absorption and utilization, the relation to Vitamin B and the health of the horse's digestive system is especially important.

The horse relies on the microbial population to produce some of the B Vitamins that it needs, including B12, which is not found in the grass and forage in which the horse eats. Research and studies do not report either toxicity or deficiency incidents being common at this time. Being a water soluble vitamin, excess production would simply pass through the urine and not remain stored in the body.

The B Vitamins are essential in supporting metabolic processes, red blood cells, and DNA. Regardless of the fact that cases of deficiency of Vitamin B Complexes are not common, it is important to note that there are proven benefits of supporting or increasing Vitamin B.

If we also consider the high concern of improper digestion and disorders on the rise, such as gastric ulcers, then we must take extra steps to support the health and proper function of the microbial populations and environment of the horse's GI tract.

Aiding the horse in the natural production of these vitamins is better than resorting to synthetic forms that could be listed on ingredient lists as: Thiamine Mononitrate, Thiamine Hydrochloride, Pyridoxine Hydrochloride, or Cyanocobalamin.

Vitamin C - For horses, Vitamin C is produced in the liver via an enzyme called L-gulonolactone oxidase. This converts glucose to Vitamin C in a healthy horse. Vitamin C is important to your horse's health not only due to it protecting cells from harmful free radicals, it also plays a role in the formation of collagen in the body.

Collagen is one of the most prevalent proteins in the body and helps support bone, muscle and connective tissue, and has even been linked to supporting digestive health as well.

As we look further into each vitamin, we can see a connection throughout the body. It can help us to see how when one part of the body is compromised, the entire system can suffer.

Vitamin D - Adequate sunshine is crucial for the horse to receive the proper amounts of Vitamin D. Vitamin D is a hormone produced by 7-dehydrocholesterol in the skin when it is exposed to the sun's ultraviolet rays. Allowing the horse to self moderate by having a shaded area to access will give the horse the freedom they need to self regulate their sun exposure.

Vitamin D supports bone and joint health because of its relation to calcium and phosphorus absorption. When watching for synthetic forms of this vitamin, look for ingredients such as Irradiated Ergosterol or Calciferol.

Vitamin E - Along with Vitamin A, Vitamin E is very popular in equine supplements. There seems to be little or no concern overall of an excessive consumption of Vitamin E and for senior horses or those showing any signs of neurological concerns, it is often the first supplement recommended.

Vitamin E is not only an antioxidant, it also supports the health and function of the nervous, circulatory, muscular, reproductive, and immune systems. Like the other vitamins horses require to maintain health, fresh grass is the best source of Vitamin E.

I have witnessed this with my mare Pokey firsthand. When she first began showing neurological weaknesses I tried many supplements that had very high doses of Vitamin E. To be honest I often saw little to no result. When we moved to our new location where she could be turned out regularly, I saw improvement. Especially in the Winter, this was usually when she struggled the most. Since being out on pasture in the Winter, she fairs very well. When trying to determine if the equine supplement you are feeding is using a synthetic source of Vitamin E, you can watch your ingredient lists for the following: dl-alpha tocopherol, dl-alpha tocopherol acetate or succinate.

Corn oil and vegetable oil are considered "natural" sources of Vitamin E, although I personally would not choose or recommend them. Utilizing fatty oils for horses is not species-specific and in some cases, can disrupt natural ratios and flows within the digestive system and the body overall when fed over a long period of time.

Vitamin K - Is likely the least talked about or noticed vitamin in equine nutrition. Its primary function is to activate blood coagulation. Vitamin K is found in the horse's hay, grass, and is also produced in the large intestine by the microbial population. If a horse experiences a deficiency in Vitamin K, it is likely a result of an upset in the microbial population in the GI tract or prolonged digestive disease. Toxicity is possible and often results in death, due to acute renal failure, although reported cases are rare.

Essential Fatty Acids - Are not synthesized by the body and must be supplied via the horse's diet. No deficiency has been reported and many supplement and feed companies are jumping on the interest of horse owners who believe supplementation of omega 6's and omega-3's could be beneficial.

It is important to review and understand where horses would naturally obtain essential fatty acids, versus increasing levels of oils or other products that we believe are a benefit to the horse.

Proteins - Are required for a wide range of purposes in the body - from hair, muscle, enzymes, hormones, nutrient transport, and more. Proteins consist of essential and non-essential amino acids. Protein is the second most abundant substance in the body after water, making up about 17-19% of the body and constituting three-fourths of the dry weight of most body cells.

Although proteins would only be utilized by the horse for energy if carbohydrates and fat reserves were inadequate, they are required for growth, reproduction, immunity, and more. It's best to determine each horse's needs and rations of protein individually, as it will vary on stage of life and lifestyle. Another factor to consider is the quality and type of protein as well. In this case, proteins that supply all essential amino acids are known as complete proteins and are ideal for equine nutrition.

Amino acids are the building blocks of protein. The body takes the amino acids and turns them into the necessary proteins it needs to help heal and repair at the cellular level. They are even an important key factor to metabolic health.

The body does not synthesize the essential amino acids, meaning it must come from the diet of the horse. Those amino acids include Arginine, Histidine, Isoleucine, Leucine, Lysine, Methionine, Phenylalanine, Threonine, Tryptophan, and Valine. While non-essential amino acids are synthesized in the body and include Alanine, Asparagine, Aspartic acid, Cysteine, Glutamic acid, Glutamine, Glycine, Proline, Serine, and Tyrosine.

Lysine, methionine and threonine are what are known as limiting amino acids. This is because if they get to a state of deficiency, your horse can't make full use of the protein for coat, hoof growth and muscle development. This means that if a horse runs out of lysine, it can't use any additional methionine. Furthermore, if it has enough lysine, but runs out of methionine, it can't use the next amino acid in line, and so on.

Trace Minerals - Adding an organic digestible trace mineral supplement to your horse's diet can have a positive effect on the hoof health, overall growth, joint and skeletal support, as well as skin and coat condition. Add to those horse health benefits that minerals also transport energy and are cofactors to enzymes, and you can start to see the importance of making sure your horse has adequate amounts of minerals.

There are two types of minerals for horses:

- Macro Minerals - Horse needs larger quantities of
- Micro Minerals - Horse requires less or smaller quantities of

Example Macro Minerals for Horses:

- Calcium (Ca)
- Phosphorus (P)
- Chloride (Cl)
- Sodium (Na)
- Potassium (K)
- Magnesium (Mg)
- Sulfur (S)

There are amounts and ratios that are important when feeding minerals to horses:

- Calcium needs to be higher than the Phosphorus in a ratio of 1.5 or 2:1. The Calcium amount can be higher than that.
- Chloride and Sodium work together as an electrolyte.
- Magnesium works with Calcium to support muscle function.

Example Micro Minerals for Horses:

- Cobalt (Co)
- Copper (Cu)
- Molybdenum (Mo):
- Zinc (Zn):
- Manganese(Mn):
- Iron (Fe):

- Fluoride (F):
- Iodine (I)
- Selenium (Se)
- Chromium (Cr)

Most horse owners believe they are feeding a balanced and complete diet. As we've discussed, most of those minerals are synthetic and are not likely to be utilized by the body properly. One processed form of minerals that is considered more digestible is chelated forms of minerals. This means the mineral is bound to an amino acid and is believed to be absorbed better. Chelated minerals can be a resolution if you're looking to boost a specific isolated mineral or group of minerals.

Ultimately, our horses are designed to obtain their nutrition from course, high fiber plants and grasses. The vitamins, minerals, enzymes, microbial population, fatty acids, proteins, amino acids, and other elements are all working together to support your horse's health and wellness.

The closest to their natural diet you can supplement and support them, the better your results will be.

SELECTING A HEALTHY BASE

Out of habit, I often refer to "graining" my horses, when in reality, there is little to no grain in what I feed. The base I use varies from horse to horse, but generally consists of a hay pellet, beet pulp shreds, and sometimes a stabilized rice bran meal.

You might wonder, "Why feed hay pellets if you're feeding hay already?" Unless you're looking to further supplement your horse, there is no need to. When you wish to support a horse with additional nutrition, utilizing soaked hay pellets as a base to add whole food nutrition and herbs to is ideal.

You'll want to watch out for ration balancers, again that gets back into synthetics. Look at the ingredient list and select a plain hay pellet.

As far as what type of hay pellet you choose will be unique to your horse. You can do extensive research on each type of grass if you wish to. What I've found over the years is some horses respond differently to different types of grasses and hays. Rather than seek to control and define what grass or hay pellet is best in my opinion, I encourage you to experiment with your horse and let their response be a determining factor.

Alfalfa would be the only pellet or even hay source that I would caution more moderation to. Here in the US, it's over-utilized and leads to many health issues when fed out of balance. It's high nutritional value and richness is simply too much for horses to intake large amounts for long periods of time.

Your horse is designed to eat high fiber, low nutritional content roughage and forage. This is not to be confused with poor hygienic quality. Referring back to what horses eat in the wild helps to reset and clarify in our minds what is best for our horses' design and needs. Many health issues in our domestic horses are a result of too nutritious of food sources and lack of exercise.

Beet pulp shreds are a great option to add to your base if you're looking to slow down the digestive system, support a horse with expired teeth, or add an additional fiber source. Remember that for your horse, adding increased fiber is a way to boost energy. This fact often seems to be misunderstood or forgotten. Beet pulp fiber is easily digestible and provides a faster source of nutrients and energy than simply feeding hay. Another benefit of feeding beet pulp is it can serve to support a diverse and balanced digestive microbiome.

A common myth of beet pulp is that it's high in sugar... While it's a byproduct of the sugar industry, by the time the sugar beet is processed to the state used to make your horse's beet pulp shreds, the sugars have been removed and extracted. That's why you'll see some manufacturers add molasses to beet pulp in hopes of making it more palatable for your horse.

When seeking to clean your horse's nutrition, sticking with a brand or option that doesn't add molasses is best. If you're feeding your horse any of the common fortified grains or pellets, it will take time to transition them to this "plain" feed approach. Think of a child that has been raised eating processed foods, cookies, candy, soda, donuts, and so on. Rarely do these kids get excited over eating their veggies. Right?

Be patient and mix in the old junk food that tastes amazing with the "good for them" foods that really are bland in taste. This will be safer for transitioning the digestive system and gut flora anyway, while increasing the success of your horse accepting the lifestyle change.

Soaking any beet pulp you choose to feed your horse is the healthiest practice. Pelleted forms may take longer to soak, which is one reason to select a shredded form instead. Some brands don't have a consistent shred size, which results in larger chunks and pieces being in your shreds. This can increase the risk of choking. See the bonus page for the latest brand recommendations.

A possible downside to beet pulp is that it can contain GMO ingredients and if you're not careful of the manufacturer you choose, the agricultural chemical remnants in beet pulp might be high. There are options available on the market that offer GMO-free, quality beet pulp for your horse.

Stabilized rice bran meal is the third and final selection you can utilize to create a more natural base "grain". Some horses benefit from increasing their fat intake, including horses with dry or creaky joints, dry coat or hooves, hard keepers, some performance horses, or horses with special dietary needs or metabolic concerns. This is an option that you actually seek to find a synthetic added to the ingredient list... Calcium is generally added as both a preservative and to help balance the calcium to phosphorus ratio.

A common question comes up about using wheat bran instead of rice bran... While I don't like to rule out ever selecting any particular feed or option completely, overall the answer would be no. If a horse needed a phosphorus increase for a temporary amount of time, I might select wheat bran. Generally, my intention is to decrease sugar and starch, while adding fat. That's why I prefer rice bran most of the time.

SIMPLE NUTRITIOUS WHOLE FOOD CHOICES

When you first transition away from a cookie cutter "all in one" nutrition, it can feel intimidating or scary. Keep exploring and empowering yourself, be sure to find like-minded supportive people to connect with. You'll find the resources to do this on the bonus page if you need help. To get you started, here are a few of the top nutritious whole food choices to support your horse when you're looking to add vitamins and minerals beyond their basic diet.

Chia Seeds - I'm curious have you tried them with your horse yet?

The chia seed has amazing nutritional value in a tiny package! Some might select chia seeds when looking for horse supplements for the coat and even equine digestive support... But there's much more to this super seed than that.

Most of the best horse supplements on the market have a long shelf life and usually it's because of a long list of additives and preservatives that make that shelf life possible. However, chia seeds have a naturally long shelf life and do not require grinding or cooking. Therefore, they make a natural convenient choice to add to your horse supplement options.

Chia seeds are a great option to support:

- Omega 3
- Fiber
- Protein
- Antioxidants
- Minerals

According to USChia.com:

- Chia seeds are the highest naturally occurring source of Omega-3 fatty acids, with a 3:1 ratio of Omega-3s to Omega-6s.
- Chia oil is 63% Omega-3, greater than flaxseed oil (58%) and menhaden fish oil (29%).
- Chia seeds are a rich source of Vitamin B, with a higher niacin content than corn, rice, and even soy.
- Chia seeds are a great source of calcium, phosphorus, magnesium, potassium, iron, zinc, and copper.

Soaked chia seeds have been a natural option I have come to trust and utilize over the years. When you're looking for a horse supplement that supports weight gain, coat, and especially during times of digestive concern, think of adding soaked chia seeds to your list of whole, natural nutrition options.

These amazing seeds can promote health by helping to soothe the GI tract, aid in the prevention of gastric ulcers and promote a balance of blood sugar levels. The health benefits don't stop there… Chia seeds can also provide support for allergy relief, improved coat, skin, hoof health, joints, and muscles.

When I feed chia seeds, I prefer to soak them, but since I often feed a soaked beet pulp shred or soaked grass pellet, this is convenient for me. The serving size I like to utilize for my personal horses is one-quarter cup (dry) chia seeds. A nice thing about chia seeds is even picky eaters are usually content with this as a supplement option.

Aloe Vera Gel or Juice - Although using Aloe vera for horses is not a new concept in horse health, there are still many horse owners who do not know the health-promoting benefits of feeding Aloe gel or juice. Let's explore why Aloe vera gel or juice makes a great natural horse supplement option, because selecting whole food based nutrition is the most effective way to get back to and maintain health long-term.

While Aloe vera is commonly known and used as a topical wound care and dressing to speed healing time for horses, it can also be a great digestive and lymph system support as a dietary option.

To select an Aloe gel or juice to add to your horse's clean supplement ration, avoid products that contain the sticky latex portion that is extracted from the plant. Often they will be referred to as "aloes" on an ingredient list. Pure, organic dietary options can be purchased at your natural grocer.

You often get what you pay for. If you're thinking of grabbing the "cheap" department or big box store brands, don't waste your money or risk your horse's health.

Aloe vera is known for being beneficial for the skin, stomach, lymph, and digestive health. It's amazingly high in digestible fiber. Due to the increasing awareness and popularity, Aloe vera pellets for horses are becoming more common. This option of use would not take advantage of the unique consistency that is soothing to the digestive system. The use of Aloe vera pellets would be easy to feed and store. More of the top equine supplements are beginning to add Aloe vera because of the awareness and understanding of its health benefits.

As with many things in natural care and the horse industry, opinions vary on whether Aloe vera can effectively be utilized in treating ulcers or other digestive concerns.

Many years ago, one of my personal horses had severe gastric ulcers, which I was told would only be resolved with medications. Since I had already tried the traditional medication route for this mare, I chose to search out herbs for ulcers, or a more natural approach. Cycling back to medications over and over again simply didn't seem logical to me.

This was prior to the study and education in natural health and care that I have now, but I cleaned her diet through removing synthetic feeds and supported her with Aloe vera gel for about 60 days. I had the vet test her about 45 days in and they reported that she was clear of ulcers, although they won't credit the diet change and herbal use for the improvement.

Historically, Aloe vera is also known for its antioxidants, anti-inflammatory, and cell protective properties. Part of this is due to the fact that it contains complex sugars called mucopolysaccharides that support cellular health and function. All of these factors express why giving your horse Aloe vera is worth some thought.

It's commonly used to help maintain a healthy digestive system and has been slowly making its way to being a common recommendation of professionals to aid in healing gastric ulcers and supporting the proper pH balance of the hindgut.

If your horse has chronic digestive concerns or has a high-stress level due to performance and travel, this natural support could make a positive difference when combined with a clean supplement ration without additives, fillers, and synthetics. What more could you want from a horse supplement option?

Kelp - If you're stressing over how to add a source of digestible minerals to your horse's diet, kelp is a possible solution. Kelp is known to contain 46 vitamins and minerals. As the trace elements of kelp are in a loosely bonded and organic structure, they are highly digestible and can be readily absorbed within the digestive system. Minerals that kelp is known to be high in include iodine, potassium, sodium, selenium, calcium, magnesium, manganese, iron, cobalt, and copper.

Spirulina - Another nutrient packed supplement choice for your horse is spirulina. This common blue-green algae is cultivated worldwide as a food source. Its name coincides with its microscopic spiral shape. Not all blue-green algae is the same. For safety reasons, ensure that you're purchasing human-grade, organic spirulina.

If you've heard of toxicity or health risks with blue-algae, it's because some species of blue-green algae do naturally produce toxins called microcystins, which can accumulate in the liver and cause liver damage.

Furthermore, other species like Chlorella, are known to be safe and nutritious, yet in comparison to spirulina will lack the high protein and immune boosting properties.

Spirulina is generally high in:

- Vitamins: A, B1, B2, B3, B6, B12, C, D, E, and K.
- Minerals: calcium, manganese, iron, chromium, phosphorus,

molybdenum, iodine, chloride, magnesium, sodium, zinc, potassium, selenium, germanium, copper, and boron.

- Amino Acids: isoleucine, phenylalanine, leucine, threonine, lysine, tryptophan, methionine, valine, alanine, glycine, arginine, histidine, aspartic acid, proline, cystine, serine, glutamic acid, and tyrosine.

From just a few whole food examples, I hope you can see that "complete and balanced" is not as complicated or hard as the industry has made it seem. If you seek to control every ration and ratio then yes, the complexity will arise. But don't be fooled into thinking that if you chart and graph every percentage and gram of a nutrient, whether synthetic or natural, that enters your horse's body that you somehow have the formula to what the body is able to absorb and utilize. There is no real day to day way to process that amount of data and information accurately.

WHOLE FOOD CHOICES TO AVOID

Just because something is a whole food, does not mean it should be a daily or regular option in our horses' diets. Things like apples, carrots, oranges - I've even seen avocados on ingredient lists of horse supplements!

As you saw in the whole foods shared in the previous section, there are times to select options that are not necessarily species-specific (something a horse would naturally encounter in the wild). When you make these selections, you should research and understand how it digests in the body and if any cautions arise that would make what you're feeding not something not to feed long-term.

Moderation is one of the 8 Laws of Health we talked about in Chapter 1 and it applies to all things we choose to add to our horse's diet. Even the pastures our domestic horses graze on are a concern and not a "true" species-specific choice.

So when you're looking into nutrition choices for your horse, it's important to know why you're selecting a certain food, herb, or supplement.

What are the pros and what are the possible cons?

How long will you choose to feed this new additive?

When will you take them off of it to evaluate your results and allow the body to balance?

The reliance of the current supplement and grain industry on ingredients such as corn, oats, and flax is a concern I frequently raise awareness to for my customers and clients.

Here in the US, the use of oats is not species-specific. Most oat ingredients or cereal grains are stripped of all or almost all of the fiber that a horse would get if they came across oats in nature, in the grass form. If you're feeding your horse oat hay or oat chaff, that is different to what I'm cautioning against.

In my experience with clients, I have yet to see a horse's health not improve when oats are removed or reduced. Most of the time these are horses that are fed rolled or crimped oats as a primary or base option.

Not seeking to vilify oats overall, it's an ingredient in the hay pellets I feed my herd at this time. Yet, it makes a small fraction less than 5% of the ingredient list, and was added to balance the phosphorus and calcium ratio. An example of knowing what you're feeding and why!

As for corn, its general analysis is 71% starch, 4% fats, 8% protein, and very little fiber at 2.2%. With that break down, I fail to see how it would serve the health of an animal that has a digestive system that relies and functions best with a high fiber diet. It might serve the digestion of livestock with differently designed digestive systems, but isn't an option I will select or recommend for horses.

Soy and flax seeds (linseed) are the last whole foods that come to my mind on common whole foods I see in equine supplements and grain that I choose to avoid. That might make you fall out of your chair, if you didn't already when I mentioned oats.

Increased phytoestrogens is the primary reason for my approach on this. Also resorting back to what I've seen in the horses I've worked with over time, this was yet another example of being open to try on something different than I saw everyone else doing.

There may be times I feed a horse flax seeds for a short amount of time for a very specific reason, but it isn't a choice I refer to often. In regards to soy, I have one product I use that has a GMO-free soybean oil in it that I keep on hand to use in times of stress or in case of colic. If it were a product that was for day to day use, I simply wouldn't feed it.

These are what I see as non species-specific choices that have proven in my experience to cause imbalance within the horse. The biggest takeaway you can have is to know what you feed, why you feed it, and be open to making changes when you get results that don't align with what you ultimately want.

CELLULAR HEALTH AND FUNCTION

Currently within the industry there's a misunderstanding or incomplete view of deficiency I would like to call attention to. A common trend in the marketplace is for you to have an analysis completed on your horse to check for vitamin or mineral deficiency.

Although I don't see this as inherently wrong, there's something you first need to look further into. Before you quickly jump only to supplementation or believing your horse NEEDS more of a certain vitamin or mineral, have you stopped to ask if there is another reason besides nutritional lack that would cause a horse to be deficient in the first place?

How well is your horse's digestive system functioning, and are your horse's cells in a state of balance or are they compromised? These are the primary factors that will determine how the body absorbs and processes nutrients, vitamins, and minerals.

So many horse owners (per a professional's recommendation) will pump their horse full of high levels of certain minerals without looking into if there is a cause in deficiency, besides a lack of availability.

If your horse's digestive system is compromised or the cells are in a state of stress or dysfunction, simply sending in more of a certain nutrient doesn't offer a solution. The body will likely send it out the backend as nutrient-rich and expensive manure…

Furthermore, if the body is able to process and absorb the nutrients, but an initial cause of the deficiency was never determined, your horse is likely to be deficient in the near future. This is a frustrating cycle I've seen many times. One I personally experienced and tried myself with Pokey before I came to the understanding and conclusion I have now.

Your horse's health begins at the cellular level. Implementing what you learn throughout this book is going to help you increase the health and function of your horse's health at its core - the cells.

Did you know that if your horse's cells were attached end to end in a continuous line… They could circle the world approximately 19 times! That's because there are TRILLIONS of cells within your horse's body.

Another important fact to understand is that each and every cell produces free radicals up to millions of times per minute. Free radicals are a natural result of living and breathing, but with the abundance of pollutions, chemicals, toxins, processed foods, and overall physical, emotional, and mental stress many horses' endure in their day to day lives, the free radical damage to the cell is getting out of control within the body.

Oxidative stress is the result of the free radicals not being balanced and neutralized within the cells. Many health conditions in both humans and horses are linked to oxidative stress.

Traditionally, we're encouraged to increase our horse's antioxidant intake to offset the free radical imbalance. You might find a few sources will recommend Vitamin C increase for horses, but the most common go-to antioxidant for horses is Vitamin E, or even essential oils.

We already discussed the concerns of adding synthetic vitamins. We also must recognize that the body can only utilize so much natural Vitamin E. Essential oils are an amazing option to use as well. But what if that still isn't enough?

It's becoming more and more apparent by the increasing levels of disease and illness, that the cells are simply in a state of dysfunction. Although I understood this truth and science of cellular health from an Equine Science class in high school, it wasn't until a few years after supporting Pokey's body back to a thriving balance that I discovered a breakthrough concept in health that is becoming more and more popular, better understood, and is very effective in promoting health.

I knew that in order to achieve optimal health for my horses, and those of my clients, there had to be more we could do naturally to support the body in maintaining health and balance. That's when a good friend of mine shared the concept of Nutrigenomics with me.

It might sound weird, and for some even sci-fi or futuristic, but there is an entire industry called Nutrigenomics that is expanding natural plant-based products that activate pathways in the body and can drastically increase health.

Activating the Nrf2 pathway is a prime example of Nutrigenomics at work. Although I won't take the time to dive into all the benefits, information, and details here in this book, I want to help you begin to expand what you think is possible for your horse's health.

It's time to think bigger, to raise your awareness to options that are available and right in front of you.

In an article published by theHorse.com, titled 'What is Nutrigenomics?', this was shared in regards to this fast growing and promising industry:

"Researchers are studying how nutrients, forms of nutrients, and nutritional strategies can influence an animal's genome," explains Kristen Brennan, PhD, project leader for equine nutrition and animal nutrigenomics at international animal health company Alltech Inc. "Our team measures what genes are turned on or off in response to feeding of nutrients, which allows them to better understand the science behind the idea that 'you are what you eat.'"

If this is a topic that intrigues you and catches your attention, you can explore to your heart's content when you visit **www. equineessentialwellness.com/bookbonus**.

Concluding this chapter, I hope it's crystal clear that cleaning your horse's nutrition serves as a crucial step to restoring or maintaining health. After years of frustration of watching my horses, and those of my clients, struggle with less than desirable results from the feeds, bags, and buckets that fill the aisles at your local feed store, there's hope. Simple solutions. More promising and longer lasting results.

Imagine your horse vibrant, full of life, and thriving… Excited for your next performance, trail ride, or session. Not running from you or facing in the corner, dragging their feet behind you like a tantrum toddler.

Once you adjust and clean your horse's diet, you will experience the differences for yourself. You will find the horse you once had or maybe the horse you always knew they could be or wanted to be.

SUMMARY & ACTION STEPS

Ultimately, the best thing you can do from what you've learned in this Chapter is to review ALL the ingredient lists from the current grains and supplements you're feeding your horse at this time.

Make a list of the synthetics, whole foods, and the mystery items that you're unsure about or may not fit in the "ate", "ide", "dl-", or Vitamin categories as shared. Remember that this isn't meant to vilify or condemn any ingredient in a feed or supplement.

But if you're feeding a highly processed grain with 10 to 20 synthetics and the whole foods listed are mostly cheap fillers like

Wheat Middlings or "Roughage Products", it's likely this feed will do more harm than good for your horse's health.

You might be wondering "What do I change to now?" Since what's available on the market is always changing and more small businesses are on the rise that are embracing more natural care, I recommend you head over to the **www.equineessentialwellness.com/bookbonus** page for the most up to date, information and suggestions.

CHAPTER THREE

The Real Pathway
to Health

THE EQUINE HEALTH PATHWAY

The digestive system is a crucial piece to health and wellness for your horse. There are two primary reasons proper digestion is important to health. First, it's the vehicle or transportation system of your horse's nutrition. Without proper digestion, nutrition will not be utilized or absorbed by the body. If the digestive system is compromised, even the best nutrition goes to waste.

The second primary reason that a properly functioning digestive system is vital to health is over 70% of the immune system resides in the GI tract. Equine digestive health concerns and issues are sadly, widespread. It's believed that 1 in 3 horses experiences mild to moderate gastric ulcers and that is just one digestive health concern from a list of many.

Hippocrates known as the Father of Medicine was quoted as saying, *"All disease begins in the gut."* That view translates over to your horse's health. Taking steps to clean your horse's nutrition, shared in Chapter 2, will serve to support a healthy digestive system. There will be less synthetics and chemicals for the body to filter and cleanse, thus reducing the work and effort to process the nutrients and transport them along the body's systems.

What else can you do to help repair, balance, and support your horse's digestive system?

THE THREE AMIGOS OF EQUINE DIGESTIVE HEALTH

For horses that regularly graze on live grass or pasture, they will get these "three amigos" naturally. But for horses that have little to no graze time, or are under higher stresses (performance horses or horses that are ill or injured, horses being hauled for long distances, and so on), these key essentials to equine digestion will need to be supplemented. To maintain proper digestion, horses need prebiotics, probiotics, and digestive enzymes.

Before we explore the details and benefits of these Three Amigos of Equine Digestive Health, it's important that you acknowledge and have an awareness of a few other crucial pieces to your horse's digestive wellness. Even the best digestive supplement for horses will be ineffective if these critical factors are ignored.

First is regular dental exams. The feeds that most domestic horses are fed are much less dense and considerably "softer" than what a horse would encounter in the wild. Because your horse has teeth that continuously grow and their diets no longer wear down their teeth properly, it's imperative that your horse have regular dental exams to ensure that they don't have long tips.

If your horse's teeth are wearing unevenly, or have protruding tips that need addressing, they can cause ulcers within the mouth. Not only do the painful sores put your horse at increased risk for dental disease and infection, they can also reduce your horse's ability to grind their food efficiently. As a result, the food matter sent through the digestive system will not be broken down and the accessibility to nutrients from feed can be dramatically decreased.

Sometimes, the best digestive aid for horses is found within their care routine. This is especially true when it comes to equine digestive health. The pH of your horse's digestive system is regulated in part by the saliva your horse produces. But your horse only produces saliva in proportion to when they are eating and grinding food.

So if your horse is like many others that experience long fasting periods of 6 to 8 hours or even longer, it's common and likely they will be at higher risk for stomach problems and other digestive concerns. Utilizing slow feeders or adjusting your horse's feed schedule alone can make all the difference in the health and function of their GI tract.

Once you've had a dental exam completed for your horse and you've adjusted their feeding schedule to accommodate their body's design, you can explore if your horse's diet contains the Three Amigos of Equine Digestive Health.

Amigo 1 - Equine Prebiotic - A prebiotic is a non-digestible food ingredient that promotes the growth of beneficial microorganisms in the intestines. It helps maintain a healthy environment for the microbial population that promotes the proper function of the horse's digestive tract. The large intestine of the horse has over 400 different kinds of bacteria, fungi, and protozoa. This is one reason it is important to feed an equine digestive supplement that supports this microbial environment.

Amigo 2 - Equine Probiotic - Animals and humans are both full of beneficial bacteria and microorganisms that promote health and balance of the body. Probiotics are strains of bacteria that are known to benefit the body. It's best if you can use species-specific probiotics when available. There are many supplements that claim to contain probiotics… If you do not see any benefits when adding it to your horse's diet, it's a red flag that either the supplement does not contain active or optimal probiotic strains, or your horse's GI tract needs additional support to balance pH and the environment of the GI tract.

Amigo 3 - Equine Digestive Enzymes - The horse's body is made up of trillions of cells, and there are different cells for different functions. Enzymes are what make chemical reactions in cells happen. They are vital for life and serve a wide range of functions in the body, including aiding in digestion and metabolism. The horse's small intestine utilizes enzymes for digestion, so it is important to supplement equine digestive enzymes, especially if your horse does not have regular access to living grass and pasture to graze.

Ultimately, your horse's microbiome diversity and balance is linked to their overall health. Extensive studies have been and continue to be conducted to explore all of the benefits and connections the microbiome has to various health concerns and conditions.

An article featured by theHorse.com shared that a study conducted by Scott Weese, DVM, MSc, Dipl. ACVIM, a professor in the Department of Pathobiology at the University of Guelph's Ontario Veterinary College reported, "...*Bacterial populations were different among the six horses studied. This finding suggests that each horse's microbiome is unique, adapted to each individual, and that a "standard" intestinal microbiome might not exist.*"

An imbalance or disruption to the gut flora can increase your horse's risk of colic, diarrhea, laminitis, and much more. Kathleen Crandell, PhD, equine nutritionist and consultant to Kentucky Equine Research in Versailles states, "*Maintaining horses on forage-based diets with minimal amounts of concentrates and avoiding abrupt change in diet are key factors involved in gastrointestinal health.*" This aligns with the principles and approaches shared within this book.

Raising awareness to how crucial a stable and diverse microbiome is to your horse should increase the understanding that the use of antibiotics, steroids, and other medications, combined with the increasing residuals of herbicides and pesticides within your horse's environment that disrupt the microbial population within the GI tract, additional supplementation of prebiotics and probiotics can be seen as a general rule of thumb to promote health and provide proper care.

Some veterinarians go as far as to suggest or perform fecal microbiota transplants, which are just as they sound. A procedure of implanting feces via nasogastric tubing or enemas to boost and balance the microbial population. I remember when I first learned of this procedure being done in people, and now horses, I can't say I find this to be a safe or natural option I would utilize for my horses or myself. But it might explain and answer a common question I receive as to why horses often eat feces when no nutritional deficiencies are found or suspected. It could be a natural way the horse seeks to balance its own microbiome.

If you find you're not sure if your horse would benefit from additional digestive support, here are some indicators to look out for:

- Your horse is experiencing high levels of stress. Whether mental, emotional, or physical. Note that even boredom or lack of exercise can increase stress for a horse.
- Your care routine has long fasting periods that are beyond your control.
- Your horse is experiencing an illness or is recovering from injury.

- When infectious sickness or viral conditions are spreading in your area and you want to boost your horse's immune system.
- You plan to vaccinate or chemically deworm your horse.

If any of the following situations align with your horse's current condition or lifestyle, then supporting them with equine digestive enzymes, probiotics, and prebiotics is highly recommended.

THE FUNDAMENTALS OF YOUR HORSE'S PATHWAY TO HEALTH

You don't have to be an expert at how your horse's digestive system works or have the anatomy memorized. But having a basic understanding of your horse's digestive system will serve you in knowing what to support and when.

Horses are classified anatomically as a non-ruminant herbivore and are most commonly referred to or described as "hind-gut fermenters," because they have an enlarged cecum that allows them to digest fibrous materials.

Your horse's digestive system begins at the mouth, which was why I shared that regular dental exams are crucial. Because from the time the horse's top lip directs the food into the mouth until the remains are sent out the rectum, it's all part of the digestive system flow and function.

After the mouth, the processed food matter progresses to the esophagus, which is a simple muscular tube that is between 50 and 60 inches in length. It conveys food from the mouth to the stomach. It moves the food to the stomach using peristalsis, which are waves of muscular contractions that squeeze the swallowed food down to the stomach.

It's important to note that your horse's esophagus only works in one direction. Meaning they can't regurgitate or vomit. Keep this in mind when you feed apples, carrots, and other large crunchy type foods that the horse may not chew well prior to swallowing, possibly causing them to choke.

The esophagus then empties into the stomach, which for your horse is relatively small and only makes up approximately 10% of the capacity of the entire GI tract. Because your horse's stomach is fairly rigid, it's important not to overfill it. It functions best when it is three-quarters full. The rate of passage is approximately 15-30 minutes. This is another reason slow feeders are beneficial to overall GI tract health.

From the stomach, the food matter moves through to the small intestine. The small intestine is an average of 70ft long and is where enzymatic digestion takes place. It's where starches, proteins, and fats are digested. Depending on the food type, the food process time for the small intestine averages from 45 minutes to as long as three hours. The quicker that it passes through to the large intestine, the less efficiently the enzymes can digest and process nutrients for the horse to utilize.

What isn't utilized by the small intestine makes its way to the hindgut or large intestine of your horse's digestive system. The large intestine of the horse is about 25ft long and makes up approximately 60% of the volume of the horse's GI tract. There are over 400 species of bacteria, fungi, and protozoa in the large intestine. Abrupt changes to the horse's diet can result in an upset of the microbial population, acidosis in the hindgut and even colic.

Within the large intestine, you have the cecum, large colon, small colon, and the rectum.

The primary function of the cecum is fiber digestion and absorption. On average, it can hold 8-10 gallons of food and water. The cecum relies on an active microbial population for the breakdown of food through the fermentation process. Food enters and exits the cecum at the top. If the horse does not have adequate water intake, this is a common site for blockage and impaction.

Like the cecum, the primary function of the large colon is fiber digestion and absorption. Microbial digestion continues in the large colon. The volatile fatty acids produced by the microbes are absorbed and used as an energy source for the horse. The large colon consists of four parts: the right and left ventral colon and the left and right dorsal colon. The bends in which these four parts connect can be another common site of blockage or impaction.

The primary purpose of the small colon is to remove excess water. It is also where the fecal balls are formed. The rectum serves as a storage for the fecal balls until enough volume is built up and the muscular contractions that have been moving the food through the GI tract cause it to empty out. The entire digestive process in the horse takes an average of 36-72 hours.

SUMMARY & ACTION STEPS

Proper dental care is crucial to digestive health. Dental exams should be performed by a qualified and licensed dental professional every 12 to 18 months. If your horse hasn't had a dental exam within that timeframe, that's your first action step from this chapter.

Because a horse's stomach is rigid and should not be over full, ensuring adequate grazing or utilizing a slow feeder is important. Also bear in mind that chewing is how saliva production is stimulated, and saliva is essential for proper digestion and GI tract health. Action step two is to review your horse's feeding schedule and lifestyle to ensure it's suited to their needs, and that long fasting periods are eliminated or reduced as much as possible.

Abrupt changes can upset the microbial balance and cause acidosis of the large intestine and even colic, so be cautious and make feed adjustments slowly.

Adequate amounts of water are crucial to proper digestion and reduced risk of impaction.

If your horse experiences digestive upset, has frequent health concerns, or is recovering from surgery or injury, it would benefit health to support with a prebiotic, probiotic, and digestive enzyme supplement. See the bonus page for the products I recommend.

PART TWO

Firewalls

You now have the core principles of understanding that you need to establish a strong foundation of health for your horse. We know for houses and buildings that foundations are crucial to the integrity of the structure. The same is true for your horse's health. Just like a building is more than simply a foundation, so is your horse's health.

Part 2 is about the "firewalls" of your horse's health. There are two different understandings of the term "firewall" outside of your horse's health. First, you have the firewall used in buildings, which is utilized to separate structures or large buildings to prevent the spread of fire by constructing a wall which extends from the foundation through the roof with a prescribed fire resistance duration and independent structural stability. Second, you might think of firewall from a technology standpoint; something that digitally sits between a computer or a local network and another network, controlling the incoming and outgoing network traffic. In this case, the firewall is a regulator that serves to control and protect.

Either view you choose to use, your horse needs the "firewalls" of their health supported naturally in order to maintain health. The core focus of Part 2 will be on parasite control, vaccination, and hoof care.

CHAPTER FOUR

Overcoming the Pesky Parasites

NATURE'S DESIGN AND PLAN

Parasites are viewed not simply as a nuisance to tolerate, but an enemy to fear and annihilate. Is this view necessary? Does nature offer suggestions and solutions for parasite control?

What if you viewed and understood that parasites are nature's "garbage men"... They are scavengers, drawn and attracted to hosts that have a desirable terrain and environment for them to live and thrive in or on?

If your horse has an abundance of parasites, it's an alarm or signal that the homeostasis of their body, or the internal environment, needs support and attention. Essentially, they have internal "garbage", or are a walking environment, that is welcoming and comfortable for the parasite to live.

It can also be a reflection of the external environment and conditions that your horse is living in as well. If there is morbid waste, manure, and ideal circumstances in your horse's external living space that's a breeding ground for parasite imbalance, the risk of your horse experiencing higher parasite loads will be increased.

The truth is, hosts and parasites are meant to coexist. It isn't beneficial for the parasite to kill off the host on which its lifecycle depends on. Ultimately, it's left unresearched or unexplored the benefits that parasites might have to your horse... There are times in that wild horses and zebras have been found to have high parasite loads, yet are seemingly healthy animals.

A majority of any studies conducted are done in controlled environments, which removes the animal's innate behavior and habits from the equation. This includes the immune system's capability to respond... A controlled environment alters the results as the animal cannot behave or respond as it naturally would on its own.

It's important to recognize that we impede and hinder our horse's ability to naturally respond as well... They don't have access to various medicinal plants that they could search out that have parasite harming and controlling properties. So it becomes our responsibility to maintain proper environment management, clean nutrition, and appropriate lifestyle to accommodate our horse's natural design.

As we are aware, the most common parasite control to the average horse owner consists of a routine schedule of deworming pastes. Although horse owners are aware of the risk of adverse side effects, and have seen or heard of a rising number of reports with severe cases of illness and some even resulting in death, they stick religiously to their routines and see it as the only solution.

Combining these risks to health and the rise of information showing that parasites are becoming resistant to these deworming pastes at an alarming rate, should leave many of us awake in the knowledge that toxic chemical warfare is not a sustainable solution.

CONTROL VERSUS TREATMENT

Would you consider your current deworming regimen parasite control or parasite treatment? You might wonder if there's a difference... For those who choose natural health, it makes all the difference! So let's clarify the difference between the two.

According to '*Principles of Veterinary Parasitology*' by Dennis Jacobs and Mark Fox:

"*Treatment is a short-term measure aimed at producing immediate* impact on the parasite population. *The intended benefit could be alleviation of suffering, enhancement of productivity or prevention of further parasite replication. Additional supportive therapy is often given to help repair damage and restore health."*

They also later clarify that:

"Although interrelated and often combined treatment and control are distinct and separate concepts."

I want to note that this reference was written by traditional, allopathic veterinarians on the overall principles of parasitology... Here's additional excerpts from this reference:

"Experience has shown that treatments rarely yield longer-term benefits if given in a haphazard or an arbitrary way. On the other hand, over reliance on routine treatments can give diminishing returns over time as parasite strains become resistant to the chemicals used."

The veterinarians that wrote this book had a clear understanding of the difference between control and treatment.

"Control has a longer-term perspective and is aimed at preventing future infection and minimizing disease risk. It implies the development and implementation plan...Non chemical approaches can augment reduce or even replace drug usage."

Yet, most horse owners don't have a consistent plan for control and what most of them hear from their vet, is how there is very little you can do to control the concerns and how consistent, regular treatments are the best and most responsible option.

When a treatment plan is needed or chosen by the horse owner, there is a complete lack of acknowledgement in the microbiome balancing and recovery support the horse needs to regain health internally. So the ideal thriving environment is more suited to breed and host more parasites.

The reason most horse owners don't embrace natural approaches is from fear and chastising from vets and other experts that make remarks such as Dr. Ramey, DVM, who on his website has a lovely blog that has this to share:

If someone has chemophobia, all chemicals are bad. In their thesaurus, the word chemical is a synonym for words like "hazardous," "toxic," or "artificial." As such, since a dewormer is a chemical, it's also bad: bad for people, horses, the environment, and bad for just about anything else that comes to mind (including parasites, too, I suppose). While a chemophobe may love his or her horse enough to try to control parasites, he or she also wants to keep from chemical exposure, too (never mind if the chemicals are safe and do their job).

Yet, directly after this statement the website has this note to the reader:

*NOTE: Dewormers are **almost** incredibly safe and non-toxic: to horses. For parasites, well, that's another thing entirely.*

I appreciate the honesty in the "almost" being accurately added to the above statement. The blog then goes on to educate that naturally you will be unable to kill and completely rid your horse of parasites.

This again goes back to the annihilation concept, and the failure to see that nature has a purpose and intention for the parasite. The goal with natural parasite control is to implement a plan to promote an environment that decreases the threat of parasite imbalance, both within the horse itself and the area in which the horse lives.

It's NOT a guarantee, or continuous treatment of a problem that may or may not exist. If at some point your horse needs a chemical parasite treatment, you do it understanding the risks, and also being prepared to support the digestive system and the body's cleansing and detoxing systems with the support they need to both clear the negative effects of the chemical dewormer and the deceased parasites as well.

COMMON PARASITES FOR HORSE OWNERS TO BE MINDFUL OF

For a horse owner to naturally approach parasite control, it's vital for them to understand what parasites the horse most commonly will confront. Some of these parasites are more prominent in some geographic regions than others. Learning what is most common where you live is another step of responsibility for you as the horse owner. Here are a few of the most common parasites horse owners should be aware of:

Bot Fly - Ever notice the little white/yellowish things on the end of your horse's mane, tail, and hair? Those are the eggs of the bot fly. How you remove those eggs is important because it is the larvae of the bot fly that is recognized as being parasitic to your horse. Utilizing therapeutic-grade essential oils on your fingers can have a smothering effect on the eggs and can help reduce the chance they will hatch. Be sure NOT to remove them via grooming tools onto areas that the horse will be grazing or eating. The eggs require the friction and moisture from the tongue and will hatch in the horse's mouth and then will later move on to the intestinal tract, but can also pass to the sinuses or the brain. Proper removal of the eggs, and natural predators like the "robber fly", bats, and small birds can help naturally control this parasite.

Strongyles (aka blood worms or red worms) - Strongyles are recognized as one of the most common parasites to infect horses. Depending on the species, the damage can range from the blood vessels and organs, including the liver. The symptoms of infestation can include anemia, colic, and weight loss. Because of the damage to the blood vessels, death can be a result of heavy infestations of this parasite. Management practices of the grazing and feeding areas is very important to reducing the risk of infestation. Keeping your soil healthy can also support an environment of earthworms and other natural predators to keep these parasites in control.

Ascarids (aka roundworms) - The eggs can be ingested from various spots in the horse's environment. Once ingested, the larvae burrow through the intestinal wall and into the bloodstream where they can then migrate to the liver, heart, and lungs. Heavy infestations of roundworms can deprive the horse of nutrients and further cause a myriad of health concerns. The symptoms of infestation can include coughing, rough coat, weight loss, diarrhea, and in foals, lack of growth and appearance of a "pot belly". Once they reach the adult stage, the females can lay up to 200,000 eggs per day that will then pass on through the feces. This lifecycle fact should bring an awareness that proper environment and manure management is the key to controlling the spread and the infestation rate of this parasite.

Tapeworms - There are three species of tapeworm found in horses. Depending on the species, they vary as to where they will reside and can be located within the horse's digestive system. Tapeworms utilize the oribatid mite to complete its lifecycle. It's actually the mite that the horse ingests while grazing. If the mite has digested feces infected with tapeworm eggs, and is then ingested by the horse, the cycle within the horse will begin. Light infestations of tapeworm can go unnoticed, but a heavy infestation can result in many digestive issues and concerns. As with the earlier mentioned parasites, manure and grazing area management is the best way to control the populations of these parasites.

Pinworms - There are many species of pinworms, the species Oxyuris equi is what concerns horse owners the most. Checking beneath your horse's tail and watching for tail rubbing is the best way to spot a pinworm infestation. Utilizing the previously mentioned environment management is key, while adding cleaning the horse's anal area with soapy water. Proper management of manure and the grazing environment are crucial.

CUSTOMIZING A PARASITE CONTROL PLAN FOR YOUR HORSE

According to PennState University, fecal egg counts provide a measure of the number of eggs being shed into the environment. A fecal egg count of zero does not necessarily mean that the horse is parasite free. The horse may have larvae or adults that are not shedding eggs and still may harbor parasites.

Fecal egg counts from an individual horse will vary from sample to sample by as much as 50%. A horse with a FEC of 1,000 may actually be shedding 500 or 1,500 eggs per gram. Low shedders are those horses that are considered to be below the threshold for deworming. Generally, between 100 to 500 eggs per gram; high shedders are generally over 1,000 EPG.

Due to the restrictive and confined area our horses are kept in, manure control is imperative. Raise your awareness to the lifecycles of parasites that are a common concern in your area.

Remember it's said that over 70% of the immune system resides in the GI tract. Implementing what you learned in Chapter 3 and supporting a properly functioning digestive system will aid against parasite imbalance. Feeding an improper diet not specific to the horse's design provides a toxic, ideal terrain for parasites to produce and thrive.

Some immunity responses aim to protect against re-infestation, this of course, implies the horse needed to be infected to build this resistance. While others aim to eliminate the existence of parasites on an initial infestation, natural parasite control is not aimed at elimination; it's intention is balance.

Don't apply what is shared within this book in a dogmatic, cookie-cutter approach way. Effectiveness comes from customizing to what you see in your horse and how they're responding. Natural parasite control is a continual care process, but I do feed through one of the following options in the Spring and Fall for my horses. I also watch for signs of imbalance and won't hesitate to support again anytime in between.

NATURAL OPTIONS FOR PARASITE CONTROL

Ground Pumpkin Seeds - Raw and unprocessed pumpkin seeds are high in nitric oxide, which is known for promoting cardiovascular health, circulation, and believed to aid in helping the body reduce inflammation. They are also considered high in magnesium and zinc, high in antioxidants, and omega-3's. All these benefits, combined with its anti-parasitic components such as cucurbitin that serves through paralysis of intestinal parasites, encourage natural elimination.

As with most of what has been shared in this book, moderation is the key to getting the benefits of these amazing seeds, while avoiding possible digestive upset with over-feeding. Suggested serving sizes should be researched and decided on individually to suit each horse's dietary needs. For my horses, I generally utilize one-quarter cup of organic, raw pumpkin seeds. I prefer to grind them prior to feeding them. Another rule of thumb for my personal care routines is to only feed these for 10 to 14 days at a time.

Diatomaceous Earth - Is made from the fossilized remains of tiny, aquatic organisms called diatoms. Their skeletons are made of a natural substance called silica. Over a long period of time, diatoms accumulated in the sediment of rivers, streams, lakes, and oceans.

My experience of DE is primarily focused only during times I suspect an internal parasite imbalance is present. There are various resources online that go into extensive detail on other health benefits believed to be associated with utilizing DE.

Ultimately, what I can share is that, I have successfully utilized DE in my parasite control plan for years. My preferred serving size is considerably smaller than what some sources recommend. For my horses, I like to use one-quarter cup once daily (twice daily if I believe the imbalance is more chronic) for 10 to 14 days. I also like to ensure that it's mixed into soaked pellets or that the horse isn't exposed to breathing in DE dry. This is a caution I had been taught many years ago, as it was believed that DE particles in their dry state could harm the respiratory system.

What leads to confusion with many natural remedies is the lack of set in stone serving sizes and that leads to conflicting information. You can choose to let this worry you or cause frustration, or you can explore further what you're looking to feed, take into account the different opinions and choose to make your own.

Taking full responsibility for your horse's health and care provides you freedom! Anytime you find yourself blaming or pointing fingers, that you made a decision based on what someone else said or suggested, you're giving your power away. Own your choices and be empowered.

You should always research and further explore what serving sizes and feeding routine is best for your horse. As a horse health coach, I serve as a guide and educator. My serving sizes are not meant to reflect standards of measurement, nor do they guarantee safety or effectiveness.

There are pre-blended herbal deworming options available online and in select feed stores. See **www.equineessentialwellness.com/ bookbonus** for the most recent product suggestions.

We discussed that supporting the body in recovery and healing after parasite treatment is necessary. These are additional steps I take that ultimately support a healthy body and are part of my parasite control plan periodically:

- Feed a prebiotic, probiotic, digestive enzymes to balance the microbiome.
- One-quarter cup Aloe gel or juice, once daily for 7 days, up to 30 to 60 days, to help balance the GI tract pH levels.
- Utilize Nrf2 activation Nutrigenomic options to help reduce oxidative stress, as an imbalance of parasites increases oxidative stress on the body.
- Gentle herbal liver cleanse to support the removal of toxins.
- Reviewing all the feeds and supplements I'm feeding my horse, understanding that an improper diet not specific to the horse's design provides a toxic, ideal terrain for parasites to produce and thrive.

Working with an herbalist or horse health coach is beneficial to maximizing your results and getting the support and guidance you need to empower yourself in making grounded and educated decisions for your horse's care.

EXTERNAL PARASITE CONCERNS

Although the same concepts shared ring true for external parasites – the external environment plays a big role with things like ticks, fleas, and so on - you can utilize natural external body sprays infused with essential oils (See **www.equineessentialwellness.com/bookbonus** for product options and suggestions).

Look into setting up tick barriers and, if possible, chickens are a great natural way to decrease external pest populations dramatically. Be extremely mindful and cautious of chemical flea and tick medications, as many adverse effects have been reported. Yet, they are heavily marketed and recommended by professionals regardless.

What about lice? In a study conducted in 2015, an article in Equus Magazine, titled 'Alternative Lice Remedies Tested Tea Tree and Lavender Oil Prove Effective in Treating Lice.' shared:

"In fact, lice infestation on those animals declined by an average of 78 percent. In the control group, which received no treatment, lice populations either stayed the same or increased."

It's unlikely that a natural parasite control program or ideal lifestyle was considered in this study. Combined with what you just learned, the results will likely improve beyond that of the study.

SUMMARY & ACTION STEPS

A natural parasite control program begins with a foundation of health. If you completed the action steps shared in Part 1 of this book, you're already on the path to creating your natural parasite control program.

You need to align your horse's lifestyle to their design and take responsibility to ensure the external environment is not a breeding ground and hot spot for parasites. Proper manure control in place and ground maintenance to keep your horse's risk of parasite imbalance lower.

You then focus on cleaning the nutrition of toxins, additives, and fillers that increase the morbid feeding ground in the digestive system, and implement steps that promote digestive health. From that place, it simply becomes an art of customizing to your horse's unique needs.

Listen, your horse doesn't live in a test tube, or controlled environment, some seasons bring the right conditions that drastically increase the risk of certain parasites. It varies region to region. The best thing you can do is understand what is a threat or concern in your area, and seek out ways to control it.

Remove the fear and panic, ask questions, and empower yourself. When you come in contact with professionals or people that wish to belittle and demean you for your choices, come back to this book and join the free communities shared on the bonus page.

There are many horse owners just like you who are ready to say no to the common ways of care that are clearly imbalanced and destructive for our horses. It isn't about vilifying or singling out what the mainstream or traditional care has to offer, it's about caring for your horse in a more natural balanced way that simply reduces the need or dependency in day to day routine care.

Let's move on to the firewall of your horse's health... Likely the most controversial topic of all.

CHAPTER FIVE

The Insider's Guide to the Natural View of Vaccination

HOW DOES SOMEONE BELIEVE THAT?

I wasn't always a chemiphobe as the vet in the previous chapter likes to refer to me and those who share my viewpoints... It's been a lifetime of real situations that led me to being more cautious and aware of what I put into my body and that of my horses.

In the introduction, I shared part of the story that brought me to what I know and do now. What I didn't share was how my first childhood dog got Parvo after her booster shots. Thankfully, she survived after a hefty vet bill and two long, touch and go weeks in intensive care. I was still in elementary school at the time, and yet smart enough to find it odd that my dog got the virus AFTER being vaccinated.

I remember the vet explaining how this can "just happen" sometimes. Only later after talking to my friend that I got the puppy from, I discovered ALL the other puppies of the litter had died of Parvo after getting vaccinated. I didn't give it much attention as a child, but that stuck with me and would later confirm that things aren't always what they seem or what you're told about vaccines.

Growing up, I still hadn't changed my lifestyle in regards to vaccines. My mother had me current on all my shots as a child, and for my animals when the post card came in the mail that they were due for their shots, I would diligently call, schedule, and get them in.

After I got married and bought my own home, I moved next door to a hearing impaired woman who later told me that she lost her hearing after a terrible reaction to a Polio vaccine. I remember feeling bad for her, but nevertheless thinking it must have been a rarity, and I thought about my childhood dog and her littermates.

Life goes on as it does... I gave birth to my son and I can admit to having increased skepticism around vaccines. But I allowed him to be vaccinated at birth (actually, I didn't know they did that, or I likely would have waited...), then came the three month, six month, nine month, and 12 month shots. Each time I took him in, the negative reactions that followed were progressively becoming more severe and frightening for me as a mother.

It first started with him screaming and crying through the night and being non-responsive or in a daze in the day. It only lasted a few days the first time and the doctor assured me everything was okay. The second time, his irritation at night and non-responsiveness in the day was more noticable and lasted over a week. The doctor still assured me there was nothing to worry about.

I started to look further into what could be happening and I saw stories of mothers who described the same things. Many of those who continued to vaccinate, trusting in the doctor's word that all was well. What was hard to accept and see was the stories of the moms whose child never came out of this non-responsive state; the ones who only wished to have their son or daughter back to being a normal baby.

My concern grew deeper, and I did as many of the sites with these stories suggested. The next time I went into the doctor, I simply asked to see the detailed pamphlet of the vaccines, so that I could read through it and ask any questions I might have. To my surprise, the doctor was not only clear, it wasn't an option I should've asked for... She proceeded to give me an earful about how educated she was and how she knew better than I did what was safe for my child.

I wished I had left the doctors office that day without vaccinating my child, but I wasn't only facing opposition from the doctor. Many of my family members, and my spouse included, did not seem to understand or support my questioning of the validity and safety of vaccines.

At the time there was even a mother in Utah who had been criminally charged after her son passed away from what I believe was Measles and he wasn't fully vaccinated. I remember someone I loved asking me, "Are you really willing to go to jail for your stupid belief?"

Although I couldn't answer yes to that question, I knew in my heart I was willing to go to jail to not have to watch my son suffer screaming endlessly through the night, or lying limp on the floor, or gazing off into the distance, not crawling around, not looking for trouble like an adventurous baby should, not baby chatting with me the latest news in pure gibberish... None of the naysayers had to experience this.

They were too busy. They had lives and work. Even my spouse refused to see or connect that this was happening ONLY after the vaccines. I remember the last time I had my son vaccinated, the effects I shared before continued for over two weeks. Because there was no fever, the doctor said that he didn't need to come and that nothing was wrong. I was overreacting.

I could hear the stories of all those moms repeating in my head... I regretted so deeply not taking a stand sooner! Thankfully, I reached out to someone who used homeopathy to support children out of these kinds of situations. It was so common that it was her sole income.

Yes, my son pulled through. Although, I still think his learning ability has been impacted negatively by adverse reactions to the vaccines. Many children are not as lucky. I still haven't received much support for my decision to no longer update my son's vaccinations. But the more I educate and empower myself, the less I care about that.

Minus one vaccine that he's never received, my son has received more vaccinations than both myself and my husband. Yet, I stopped his updates at 18 months. It's time to wake up and realize what's happening. It's happening to children, pets, and, yes, your horses.

It seems crazy to think that I still vaccinated my animals regularly without much thought to if the vaccines could be having a negative impact on their health like it did with my son... It's funny what we choose not to see at times.

Then, one day, a past client of mine called me in tears, explaining that her horse had just dropped over dead after a recent "routine" vet exam. Within minutes of this horse receiving a round of various vaccines, the horse literally dropped over dead. She was told there was nothing that could be done, and that the horse must have had a rare, possibly allergic reaction to one of the vaccines.

I get that until this happens to you, until you have to experience these circumstances yourself, or you have to support someone through it who does, it might be easy to brush it off as "rare". But when you get in the line of work of supporting horse's back to health, like I do now, the stories are so common and prevalent, there is NO denying. Unless you choose to continue to believe it's a coincidence and has nothing to do with the safety of the vaccines themselves, then take a deeper look.

BEYOND STORIES

Now comes the time when some people want more than just a story… After more than 17 years of working with people, I've come to see patterns in human behavior.

First people want to hear stories, then they choose not to believe the stories. So they search for proof and facts. When the proof, facts, and science don't align with what they want to be true, they simply disregard the story and the facts altogether. At this moment in time, our society is in the state of disregarding real stories, historical facts, and scientific proof of the lack of validity and risks of vaccines.

Remember that illusion of control I keep talking about? Here it is again… The illusion that we can control viruses or nature in general is quite comical really. This concept really settled in with Louis Pasteur, who was a French chemist and microbiologist renowned for his discoveries of the principles of vaccination, microbial fermentation, and pasteurization. The history and background of Louis Pasteur is one full of deceit, power, connection, and plagiarizing.

Sadly, Pasteur's flawed and disproved germ theory is still what medical professionals are taught to this day. The germ theory is the basis and foundation of modern medicine.

The monopolization and control continued with the money, power, and influence of John D. Rockefeller, Fredrick Taylor Gates, and Andrew Carnegie. Through utilizing the "The Flexnor Report" and only funding programs, schools, and research that favored their own petrochemical companies as the "cure", they shaped and molded an educational and medical system in which they controlled the competition and the knowledge of medical physicians and veterinarians.

There is an alternative theory, that if it was better known and understood, would revolutionize the way people look at disease, germs, and pathogens. The concept and theory of pleomorphism.

Pleomorphism was developed by French biologist Antoine Béchamp, Louis Pasteur's largest counterpart. Unlike Pasteur's belief that germs and pathogens are something we need to fear and wage war on, Béchamp discovered that it's the environment of the cells that will determine health or disease. By improving what Béchamp called the 'milieu', the environment of the cells, the so-called pathogens, did not disappear, but aided in repairing the cells.

What we focus on grows, in the case of health, the same concept is true. Through focusing on health instead of disease, Béchamp discovered that the pathogens or microorganisms worked towards health, instead of disease. When Béchamp focused on eliminating the disease or pathogen, they would become stronger, harder to combat, and even morph. Through supporting a healthy cellular environment and cell regeneration, wellness can be restored without attacking or combating disease, bacteria, or pathogens. When symptoms of disease surface, it's a sign that the environment of the human or animal cells is toxic, and needs to be restored and set to balance.

The germ or pathogen is nature's way of cleaning morbid matter from the body. In Chapter 4, we talked about a parasite being the "garbage men" for the body… Pathogens and viruses are the same, simply at the cellular level.

Attacking and destroying the garbage men will only leave more garbage. The right thing to do then, is to deal with the "garbage", the morbid matter and environment. Support the body with proper nutrition, get the blood and lymph flowing, and naturally aid the body into a homeostasis where morbid matter ceases to exist. Germs and pathogens will then not have what they need to thrive, and are no longer needed by nature to bring balance and will no longer be a concern, even if they are still present in the body.

"Bacteriologists are unanimous in declaring that various disease germs are found not only in diseased bodies, but also in the bodies of seemingly healthy

persons." ~ Dr. Henry Lindlahr

Since our current medical system is not based on Béchamp's theory, society is taught and encouraged (sometimes required) to use vaccinations, toxic preventive care measures, antibiotics, and other toxic drugs and chemicals to kill or fight pathogens, bacteria, and viruses.

As mentioned in the previous paragraph, attacking these "intruders" only strengthens the pathogens and causes them to get stronger and even morph. Meanwhile, the patient gets weaker and their body becomes unable to process cell restoration and regeneration, because the cellular environment continues to become more toxic and only fuels the disease and illness further. "Superbugs", like MRSA, are real life examples of the morphing and strengthening that can occur with pathogens and only seems to support the work of Antoine Béchamp; proving that focusing on disease and illness will only grow more disease and illness.

Understanding the importance of the terrain, and that the health of the cell and its environment, is crucial to those who want to promote health naturally. Cells are the smallest functional units of the body, so small that they require a microscope to be seen and studied. These tiny units play a large and crucial part in the health and function of the body.

WHEN DRIVEN BY FEAR...

If you could take away only one thing from this book, it would be to have extreme caution when society, an industry, or a person is trying to scare you into something. I remember when I first took my business online, I did a webinar on equine gastric ulcers.

In the email series leading up to the webinar, I shared statistics of the number of horses that currently experience gastric ulcers... I received a heated reply and quickly after, another message via Facebook on how I should feel ashamed that I had to resort to "scare tactics" to get people interested in my webinar.

To clarify, if someone is using truth, unbiased real life numbers or facts to educate and empower you, that is not a scare tactic. I've shared before in this book that I have no intention to convince or force any of the concepts shared in this resource.

I'm simply expressing and sharing what I've learned, experienced, and found on my journey in my personal life and serving as a horse health coach. What you decide to implement or leave out is 100% up to you.

I regularly work with students and clients who still consistently feed fortified grains, others who still use chemical dewormers, and those who regularly vaccinate their horses. This is not about shaming, guilt tripping, or bullying people to act or believe in a certain way.

I shared my experience with the doctor when my son was a baby... I, to this day, receive that same condescending treatment from veterinarians, trainers, farriers, friends, and even family. You likely will as well, especially on the topic of vaccinations, should you ever decide that you're not totally on board for what they claim they are.

When force, fear, or intimation is required, there is often lack of truth, understanding, and an agenda at hand. They can't educate and empower, as only one side can be heard. Because if both sides are heard at the same time, theirs doesn't add up.

When education and empowerment is at the base and root of something, freedom of choice is available and responsibility and power remains intact. So let's explore vaccines for a moment, from a new perspective rarely talked about... The viewpoint of the immune system.

After all, the immune system is one of the major "firewalls" of the body. Ultimately, the immune system is what's impacted from vaccines. So wouldn't understanding how the immune system works and how it experiences vaccines serve in the decisions we make in the matter?

By definition, vaccine is any preparation used as a preventive inoculation to **confer immunity against** a specific disease, usually employing an innocuous form of the disease agent, as killed or weakened bacteria or viruses, to stimulate antibody production. ***The truth is if vaccinations did ensure immunity, the person or animal that was vaccinated would not be concerned or threatened by those who aren't.*** Yet, in today's society, the unvaccinated people and animals are blamed for spreading disease among those who are already vaccinated. There is a complete lack of common sense or logic within this fear.

If a vaccine confers immunity, there should also be no cases of those who are vaccinated getting the disease, which there are. This is currently the "strongest" argument that those who wish to force vaccination have; is convincing the general public that those who are unvaccinated are posing a risk.

The only threat an unvaccinated person or animal would have to society would be to other unvaccinated people or animals. At which point, they would all get the disease they weren't vaccinated for and all that would be left is safe vaccinated people and animals.

That's what doesn't add up. Vaccinated animals and people do get sick. So what's happening, why don't they have immunity like they "should"?

THE IMMUNE SYSTEM BASICS

Truth be told, humans have yet to fully comprehend and unravel the complexity of the immune system. It's not my intention to turn this into an immunity reference guide. But to grasp why immunity is not guaranteed to be conferred by vaccination, you must have some core truths about the immune system.

Most of us were taught that the primary function of the immune system is to keep out and block pathogens from the body; to kill and eliminate pathogens that enter the body (sometimes only if they get out of balance).

In pursuit of control and domination, humans seem to have a complete disregard for nature and its design. Yet, if we want to exist and thrive in and with nature, it's important to understand nature's design and purpose for things. There is an order, a system, and flow to everything in nature. Even the immune system is designed to function in a certain way; each part serves as a piece of conferring immunity.

For the basic breakdown in this book, we need to recognize two parts of the immune system: the innate and the adaptive parts.

The innate immune system is made up of the skin, mucus membranes, and stomach acid. These are designed to be the FIRST line of defense for the immune system. The SECOND line of defense for the immune system is the inflammatory response and phagocytes (antigen-presenting cells).

The next part of your horse's immune system is the adaptive immune system. This is the part of the immune system with "memory". It serves to detect various strains and types of pathogens that have entered the body before. It utilizes B-lymphocytes and T-lymphocytes and a complex synergy that happens between these cells.

"The immune system is truly a remarkable entity and very complex

at that. Blood, bone marrow, spleen, thymus, liver, lymph system are all involved. It is never just one part of the immune system that responds to the foreign invader; various cells, antibodies, and chemicals create functional unity. We can say that the immune system is not so much an organ complex, but the intelligent communication between all of the organs." ~ Aleksandra Mikic, DHHP, DVHH, DPh, Author of '*How To Immunize Your Dog Without Vaccines*'

The basic premise of vaccination is that if you inject a virus into a human or animal, it will become immune to the disease and is not at risk of further infection. The flaw here lies in the delivery system by which you bypass the first and secondary responses of the immune system altogether. Because the design of the body and immune system have, therefore, been violated, consequences are put in place.

Let's for a moment recognize that most of us have two arms. Although they are similar, each is unique and serves a purpose. Would you remove one, simply because you have two? Which is more important to you?

Yes, you can function with one, but they function best together. The immune system is much the same way.

Imagine for a moment that your horse's immune system is a secure, alarmed, locked, protected home. Would it strengthen the security to repeatedly assist criminals and threats through a secret entrance?

Over time, that would simply weaken and render useless the other parts of the security system; also leaving those defending the home in a highly agitated and over-sensitive state (for example, autoimmune disease).

Injecting foreign material into the body is repeatedly breaching the body's security system over and over. It will have a negative impact on your horse's immune system and overall health. If the immune system becomes overactive and develops antibodies against its own tissue and cells, like collagen and DNA, a myriad of health concerns will arise.

This is happening not only because of the bypassing and disruption to the order and design of the immune system, but because of the ingredients in which we are injecting DIRECTLY into the bloodstream.

REVIEW THE LIST OF INVADERS YOU'RE INJECTING INTO YOUR HORSE'S BLOODSTREAM

The natural order and design is NOT the only concern when it comes to vaccines. Remember in Chapter 2 we discussed the importance of ingredients. The products you use on your horse and feed your horse has a big impact on their health!

Do you think the same would be true for something you're choosing to inject into the bloodstream? You are pushing and giving these ingredients access past the blood brain barrier and direct access to the cells and DNA. Notice the direct responsibility I'm placing here as I say "you"... This might feel uncomfortable. But we, as horse owners, can no longer bury our heads in the sand and point fingers on what "they" have done to our horses.

You are your horse's advocate. Anything you choose to put in their body is 100% your responsibility. So before your horse has a severe reaction, drops over dead, or has a vaccination-induced laminitic episode, you need to inform and empower yourself in what you will choose for your horse.

You might not even realize it.., but some of the vaccines on the market are literally genetically modifying your horse's DNA. I share a screenshot of the CDC website in my 30 Day Equine Health Transformation course of the common listed ingredients in vaccines. As I went to write this book, I saw that they have drastically changed and softened much of what's listed there.

I encourage you to ask for the full pamphlet for any injection you intend to give your horse. Things you might find like aluminum, mercury (listed as Thimerosal), acetone, bovine calf serum, formaldehyde, egg protein, and so on.

The recent updates to the CDC site appear focused on encouraging you how safe these ingredients are as they are naturally found within the body or within the foods you can safely consume. But make no mistake, injecting these ingredients into your horse's bloodstream, or your own for that matter, is no comparison to food you eat or elements that safely exist within the environment.

The information on the CDC website is primarily for human vaccines. With basic online searches, you're not likely to find the ingredients contained within equine vaccines. Once you have the truth about the ingredients and you understand that vaccination violates the natural processes of the immune system, you can make an informed and grounded decision on what you feel is right for your horse.

WHAT OPTIONS OR ALTERNATIVES DO YOU HAVE?

Supporting a healthy immune system and balanced lifestyle for your horse is crucial to your horse's overall health. After educating yourself on the ingredients of vaccines and raising your awareness that they violate the process and function of the immune system, you might wonder what options you have.

There are alternative options available. Be aware that these are heavily scrutinized by the mainstream as ineffective and useless. You'll see resources questioning and pushing for proof, studies, and research. There is no large industry looking to fund or prove that there are alternatives to vaccines. But even if there were, there would be plenty of naysayers and studies to disprove anything that challenges vaccination.

I have seen this done on valid studies on natural remedies all the time. There are studies available showing the effectiveness of certain herbs, essential oils, and nutritional supplements that I share and use as references in my blogs and courses. Yet, it never fails how quick people are to find a doctor or academic expert that can spin the research as invalid in some form or fashion.

I'll be open and state I haven't utilized either of the options shared below, yet many of my customers and clients have. I live in an area where there isn't a high amount of common infectious diseases that I feel my horses are at risk of… I also don't currently travel much with my horses or have them in contact with strange horses outside our herd.

But since I work with people from across the country and around the world, as well as trainers or horse owners who compete or travel, they often have the need or requirements to go beyond what I choose for my personal horses.

Nosodes - Are an option to utilize. They are a homeopathic remedy from a discharge from an individual with the disease. This means it isn't simply the virus or pathogen alone, it contains the tissue or fluid of the organism that the nosode was formed from as well.

This serves to provide the horse with energetic properties and the essence of the pathogen or virus. The nosodes are believed to serve as a way to allow the body to experience the disease in a more natural way. Avoiding violating the immune system's processes and forcing through the blood brain barrier via an injection.

To clarify, they are not a replacement for a vaccine, nor are they utilized for the intention of long-term protection or immunity. They are designed and intended to be used shortly before exposure or shortly after suspected exposure to the pathogen or virus.

Most studies that have been conducted on nosodes are poorly planned and executed with clear ignorance to how the nosodes are intended to be used. Homeopathic remedies are most effective when utilized under the guidance of an experienced professional.

Commonly utilized nosodes for horses include Flu, Rhino, Eastern & Western Encephalitis, Tetanus, Strangles, Potomac Horse Fever, Botulism, West Nile Fever, Herpes, & EPM.

Please see the bonus page for more information on homeopathic professionals that can support you if you choose to utilize nosodes for your horse.

Titers - Can be a great tool to gauge if your horse has antibodies and immunity. Once your horse establishes a protective titer, there is no need for additional and further assessment. As immunity is conferred life long.

Like anything else designed to naturally support a healthy life without dependency on Western medicine and vaccines, the use of titers has a swarm of conflicting opinions and debate surrounding the topic.

Ultimately, there is NO perfect answer that will ensure immunity for your horse. As we mentioned, the immune system is complex and there are still limitations to what can be tested in regards to if your horse is immune to a disease or pathogen.

One of the reasons titers are not fully supported, or some deem them unreliable, is a horse with a low titer still has the chance of being fully protected. The protection or immunity can be the result of a process of cellular immunity, which is not something that can be measured or analyzed effectively at this time.

Finding a titer supportive veterinarian can prove to be a challenge, as many refuse to acknowledge titers as a legitimate science. Much like fecal egg counts for parasite control, it's most effective to utilize titers as a tool to assist and guide your decisions, not be used as an absolute.

SUMMARY & ACTION STEPS

The illusion of control and certainty… Are you beginning to see the signs and patterns in every area of your horse's care?

The only action step for this Chapter is to decide what you believe is best for your horse in regards to safeguarding their immune system, while still feeling you're taking action to help establish immunity. There will be additional resources available on the bonus page if vaccine safety and effectiveness is something you wish to explore further.

In regards to immunity, vaccinated or not, your horse is NOT guaranteed to be immune from infectious disease. Explore and empower yourself. From that place, you will make the best decision for your horse. The most important thing is don't blindly choose, or worse, make decisions from pressure or fear imposed from people who won't have to face the consequences or results of the choices that you make.

You must get to a place where you have peace and feel grounded in the choices you make with your horse's care. Then, regardless of what may come in your horse's health journey, you will know that you did your best.

CHAPTER SIX

The Secret Impact of Metal in Our Horses' Lives

NO HOOF, NO HORSE AND STRAIGHT FROM THE HORSE'S MOUTH

Now, we go back to the beginning, the phrase "healthy as a horse", the horse, a species known and cherished for strength, freedom, agility, power, and longevity. Capable of surviving in harsh, rugged environments, while traveling miles and miles every day. How does a creature with this persona and embodying such characteristics become a statistic of having an average "performance life" of 3 to 6 years in a life span of 20 to 30 years when domesticated?

All the while within that life span experiencing many health concerns, lameness, and injuries. The modern answer to this problem is to "improve" upon the horse through breeding, mechanical devices, and various drugs to help these weak and struggling animals.

Would it not be more advantageous to improve our ways and our domestic horses to mirror more of what is seen in the wild horse? To alter how we impact their lives and what we can do to improve the methods, environments, and expectations we require of the horse that we chose to contain and domesticate?

This question can bring a long list of concerns that a horse owner should think about and research in relation to how their horse is designed by nature to live and thrive. For the focus of this chapter, it's my intention to focus merely on two points that have a major impact on many domesticated horses.

First, what is the impact of metal that we place in the horse's life? Specifically, in relation to bits in a horse's mouth, and metal shoes applied to the horse's feet. Second, are we aware of how these things affect the health of the horse?

Together, let's explore the ramifications and scientific facts to gain a better understanding of how people are affecting the horse with the metal they place in their lives.

BITS OF INFORMATION YOU LIKELY NEVER KNEW

Beginning at the mouth, it's understood that the horse's mouth is one of the most sensitive areas of the body. With that knowledge, what would lead people to putting a bit, especially one of metal into the horse's mouth? For some, it's the mere fact of control, riding a 1000lb prey animal, psychology would naturally lead one to want to have control.

Placing metal in a sensitive area such as the mouth, gives leverage and control to the rider.

For the softer, more natural-minded folks, it's out of sight, out of mind. From personal experience, this would be the case for me. It had not crossed my mind it would cause pain or concern, as I have been taught that the horse's mouth is even designed to carry a bit.

After recently purchasing a horse with a large piece of his tongue missing, due to the improper use of a bit, I became aware of the damage that could be done. With that horse, he had behavioral concerns and issues anytime a bridle was presented, and understandably so.

Per the work of W. Robert Cook, FRCVS, PhD, my horse is not alone, his findings have documented over 100 ways in which a horse shows, by behavior, that the bit is causing pain.

These horses can suffer in silence as it's in their nature to endure and tolerate pain in a way that would not alert predators to their vulnerability and weakness. Because of this natural characteristic of the horse, the horse owner must be aware of and able to perceive and understand subtle communications from the horse.

Injury to the horse's tongue is only one of the many concerns that can be caused by the bit. Looking at the anatomy where many believe the horse to be designed to carry the bit, it is important to note that the bars in which the bit lies are not flat as we may be taught or think; neither are they round and fleshy. The bone is more comparable to the structure of the human shin.

In Cook's research of jawbones from museum collections, those of wild horses did not have signs of bone spurs, although the incidence in the bitted horses was high. Another study of 35 zebra skulls showed no sign of bone spurs. These findings bring a clear awareness that the anatomy of the horse is not designed to carry a bit and that the use of bits is having a negative impact on the horse's health. Other effects of the bit include lack of oxygen and bleeding from the lungs, which causes undue stress and concern to the overall health and wellbeing of the horse.

One who has been conditioned to believe that bits are a necessary part of horsemanship, or form of communication and control, must find a way to open their mind to a new thought. An awakening to the bit as an impediment to communication and hindrance of control.

We are led to believe out of lack of time and skill to develop communication with the horse, that we must instead rely and turn to mechanical means of force and intimidation; a lack of willingness from the horse owner to establish the knowledge and understanding of the horse's language, expressions, and reactions. While in our illusion of control, the bit can instill fear and, therefore, a stronger flight response, as in the case of the horse I purchased. Any contact with his mouth caused an emotional, borderline uncontrollable flight response that was a danger to the horse and the rider.

Through genuine horsemanship, relationship, bond, and connection, horse and rider can learn to communicate and understand each other. Liberty work and ground work can develop and build the riding work. The use of crossover bridles and bitless bridles can replace the use of metal bits. Then the horse can still be utilized and enjoyed in a domestic setting, without the negative, painful, and harmful effects of metal in his mouth.

Horsemen Mark Rashid described the goal in achieving softness and communication with horses:

"Instead of being the boss, be a leader, because a leader can be trusted. The way to develop trust is through consistency. If you're consistent, you're dependable. If you're dependable, you become trustworthy. If you're trustworthy, the horse will be at peace with you. If the horse is at peace with you, then he can be soft."

He continues by explaining the difference between softness and lightness:

"Lightness can be trained, and is what we most commonly see. Lightness is present when all is well and the environment is one in which the horse feels safe. Softness on the other hand is present and available at all times. Through training we take the softness out of the horse and spend the rest of our lives trying to put it back."

IS NATURAL HOOF CARE SUSTAINABLE FOR YOUR HORSE?

That leads us to the next area of the horse in which humans have practiced placing metal, the hoof. No hoof, no horse is a common phrase in the horse world. After some study and understanding of the healthy hoof, one would wonder how metal shoes ever became a part of the mainstream care of the horse.

Scientifically, the practice of metal shoes is almost a guarantee of no hoof left for the horse. It also promises a future of navicular syndrome, white line disease, wall cracks, thrush, and other hoof concerns. Diet and lack of movement contributes to these concerns, but it is not through the fault or design of the horse as some have been led to believe.

Most horse owners, including myself, begin having a horse shod because we have been taught and told that it will protect the horse's hoof and save it from excessive breakdown from the amount of work we put our horses through. It's a practice caused by fear and habit. The need for metal shoes comes from the use of metal shoes that weakens the structure of the hoof.

Historically placing metal shoes on horse hooves was done because of the wet and confined spaces the horses were kept in caused the hoof to deteriorate. Over time, it became a sign of nobility, now it remains more of a fad or thing that people do simply because they see others do it. The horse had been utilized without the use of metal shoes 7,000 years before shoes were invented.

If the metal shoe does not provide protection for the horse's hoof, what does it do? To understand this fully, we need to understand the healthy, natural hoof. The hoof is more than just protection and a basic anatomical end. For the horse, it works as a circulatory pump and expands and contracts as it contacts the ground. It's important to see the hoof as an organ and seek to understand its internal structure, purpose, and function.

Mentioning here the circulatory part that the natural hoof plays in the horse's body, it's a relevant time to discuss basic bone anatomy. Cortical bone is extremely dense and strong, designed to withstand forces of bending. Under the hard, solid layer of cortical bone is "spongy bone"; it's given its name from the fact it looks like a sponge but the name bears no resemblance to the texture or feel, as spongy bone is very strong and solid. Inside the spongy bone, there will be pockets of bone marrow and vessels for circulation, which nourish the bone and maintain its strength and health.

By reducing or interrupting the circulation of blood to and through the hoof, adverse effects result up the skeletal portion of the leg and can increase the risk of injury and weaken the skeletal system overall.

Proper hoof health begins from the inside with adequate and species-specific nutrition combined with movement and external hoof care that mimics nature as much as possible. Much like nutrition and health care, hoof care and trimming should be as unique as the individual horse and hoof. Learning and understanding how nature designed the hoof to be, followed by trial and error, is how you master truly natural hoof care.

The hoof should be short, with little or no hoof wall extending past the sole. The bars should gradually descend toward the wide frog, which should have a rawhide-like texture. The heels should be low and the sole concave. The hoof should be smooth, free of chips, splits, or flares.

This basis for the hoof is modeled after the wild horse. Wild horses have longer life expectancies than domestic horses and often are not plagued with navicular, founder, white line disease, and other afflictions of the hoof.

How then does the metal shoe effect or interact with the hoof and overall health of the horse?

Traditionally, the shape or model of the hoof differs from the natural design when looking to put shoes on. Raising the heels and having longer toes is the norm, which works to tear the hoof from its proper place and begin the shifting of the coffin bone and destruction of the lamina.

Metal shoes also cause restriction of the expansion and contraction of the hoof, causing a reduction in the circulation and blood flow. That leads to a reduced perception and feeling in the hooves, raising the risk of improper biomechanics and injury.

Metal has its own properties that can be damaging to the horse. The top three concerns would be it conducts heat and cold, it conducts electricity that can shift or interrupt the vibration and neural pathways of the body, and it lacks the ability to bend or flex, which increases the vibration and shock sent through the body, bones, and joints.

The metal shoe is not the only health concern to the horse in relation to traditional trimming.

The goal of some more traditional farriers is to change the natural angle of the hoof. Even if they are not applying metal shoes, they can cause bone remodeling by shifting the angle of the hoof over time.

The coffin bone provides structural support and an internal mold for the hoof. From an x-ray, it looks like a mini hoof inside the hoof. It also transmits weight up the skeleton of the leg. Ideally, the coffin bone should be parallel to the ground in the hoof capsule, or as close as possible for each individual horse. Conditions that result in the loss of bone tissue in the coffin bone are devastating, because loss of substance from this bone typically cannot be recovered. The change in the architecture of the coffin bone results in pathologic adaptations of the hoof and its supporting structures.

TOO MUCH TOO SOON

Anyone who values performance or longevity of the horse should want to optimize circulation through unshod hooves, and support ample oxygenation and breath by means of bitless bridle options. The studies and research showing the damage of metal in horses' lives should lead all horse owners to alternative more natural options.

Alongside these two topics is also the need to understand the growth plates and bone maturity, or growth time. The mentioning of the short performance life is also in relation to horses being asked too much too soon in life. In young, growing animals, the bone is working via osteoblasts to deposit and calcify bone, causing the bone to grow longer and wider. Upon reaching maturity is when this separate plate will fuse and is incorporated into the spongy bone portion. This is when the bone is considered fully mature.

Undue stress to these bones can affect their strength and compromise the integrity of the anatomy and structure. After birth, the bones continue to grow until the animal reaches maturity. Each animal has different maturity rates and, in the horse, there are growth and maturity plates that do not fuse or come to maturity until the age of five. Most horses are started much younger than that and are worked vigorously by that age. It's no wonder that horses breakdown anatomically and are unsound both mentally and physically at such young ages.

As horse owners, we should look to be an improvement and benefit to the horse's life, but the vast amounts of illness and injuries our domestic horses struggle with awaken the reality that this is not the current case. Horses need us to change this status, and it can be done through awareness and taking responsibility.

The scales of tradition and status quo will shift as more horse owners come to an understanding that there are better, healthier options that are more aligned to the horse's design and nature. Supply and demand will eventually take over, but until then it's the responsibility of those of us who have found these studies and information to lead by example, educate, and share with those who are open and ready to learn.

SUMMARY & ACTION STEPS

On the bonus page, you'll find resources on exploring more about natural hoof care. Finding a barefoot trimmer can be a challenge in some areas, but thankfully it's a growing field with promising professionals on the rise.

As far as going bitless, I will admit I haven't transitioned there completely. Much like the rest of this book, my intent isn't to vilify, but to educate. Many of the myths I had been taught since I was young were shattered with what I discovered and shared with you here in this chapter.

It brings a new awareness to the importance of the feeling and lightness you should have when riding with a bit... And at least for me this information served as an eye opening refresher to what horses suffer and experience at our lack of knowledge, or desire to move faster and accomplish more.

Isn't it interesting that we even found the illusion of control in the use of bits? Ultimately, the action steps of this chapter are for you to evaluate where you stand on these areas of your horse's care and your riding practices.

You might choose to explore these concepts further, make major shifts, or continue on the same path as you were before. Awareness and empowerment continues.

PART THREE

Finishing Touches and Customization

Now that you've established a strong foundation of health, you have the framework in place for a healthy lifestyle, and you have secured your horse's firewalls of protection. It's time to add the finishing touches and get to customizing your horse's care to their unique needs.

Rarely does anyone focus on all three parts of health... That's why most programs and approaches that are shared appear to only work sometimes or for certain horses.

What makes a house a home is the customization and finishing touches. You don't want to skip over or leave these out. But you also can't slap finishing touches on a home with a cracking foundation or faulty framework.

Maximize your results with your horse's health by tying in the final three chapters of this book.

CHAPTER SEVEN

What Tends to Get Overlooked

DON'T SHOOT THE MESSENGER

Have you ever been talking to someone who heard what you said, but they weren't really listening? This is what often happens with our horses' health. We talked about this in the beginning chapters of this book, but there are a few more key concepts to natural health you should know about as you begin embarking on a more natural approach to your horse's care.

Any symptoms that your horse presents is a messenger to what's happening within the body. So you don't want to shoot the messenger... In this case that means don't mask, treat, or suppress it. Symptoms are a warning and alarm to the state your horse's body is in. Anytime you choose to mask, treat, suppress, or ignore the symptoms, the disease state will be left unresolved and will get worse.

Your horse's symptoms are a visible representation to what is happening inside the body. This concept has been known and understood by true health focused practitioners for thousands of years. In Naturopathy, it's referred to and understood through what's known as Nature Cure and in Traditional Chinese Medicine (TCM), the Law of Integrity.

Nature Cure views health as balanced and harmonious vibrations of the elements and forces of the body on the mental, physical, and emotional levels, in alignment with the constructive principle of Nature within the body of the horse. The Constructive principle in Nature builds up, is growth, improves upon, repairs, rejuvenates, and restores. This principle balances out the destructive principle in Nature.

That means that disease is the imbalance and disruptive vibration of the elements and forces of the body on mental, physical, and emotional levels, in alignment with the destructive principle of Nature within the body of the horse. The destructive principle of Nature breaks down, mutates, deforms, stagnates, pools, settles, and decays.

At any given time in your horse's care, you're either working to support the constructive or destructive principles of Nature.

With Traditional Chinese Medicine, you can look to the Law of Integrity, which is the understanding that what's happening on the inside of the body will ultimately be seen outside the body, because the body is an integrated system of synergy and connection. This is further detailed down with supportive theories, including the Five Element Theory, which gives structure and pattern to seasons, temperatures, organ systems, tissues, and orifices to guide and interpret what is happening with the body. Then continuing with the Theory of Yin & Yang, which shares similar thought patterns to the constructive and destructive principles of Nature, only it's taken even deeper, expansive, and detailed.

The foundation beliefs of natural health are historical, passed down, and relevant. Over time, we have been conditioned to feel these options are the last resort, because traditional treatments aggressively suppress symptoms, giving an illusion of improvement.

There's an ever increasing regulation being put on natural health practitioners, claiming to be in the protection of people and their animals... If what we do doesn't work, people would naturally quit coming and we would be eliminated from the marketplace.

Let's be real, your horse didn't get sick overnight, even if it felt like they did. It often seems sudden and out of nowhere because we are taught that the little symptoms or minor symptoms are no big deal, and we treat them or ignore them altogether. It will take time to recover your horse's health and vitality.

There are also some things you should be prepared for as you seek to improve your horse's health. As you work backwards through the steps the body took to getting sick, things might appear to get worse BEFORE they appear to get better. This is often referred to as a Healing Crisis. Older symptoms can represent themselves as your horse is on the path to recovery.

There is a lot that happens from point A (*health*) to point B (*disease*). The time it takes for the body to recover from illness is connected to the time it took to develop it... The tricky thing is that it could've been over a span of years that you didn't know it was developing.

As you're supporting your horse's health and holding a space for them to recover, the goal you typically are seeking is for disruptions or symptoms to flow progressively in one of the following patterns:

- Vertically - From head (top) to feet (bottom), or rump to feet.
- Laterally - From head (front) to tail (back).
- Depth - Of symptoms from more internal (more serious) to external.

Mental improvement is an important indicator as well. It can give you indications of the will and the ability the horse currently has to pull through the disease state. As symptoms move more external, they are often more visible to us and those around us, and, naturally, we want to suppress them back in. RESIST that urge and recognize where you are.

If older symptoms do arise, make note and monitor the duration and intensity. If the older symptom is remaining strong and persistent, it's likely time to adjust your remedy, nutrition, or other areas.

This should seem a little like a review from Chapter 1... But, in my experience in working with horse owners one on one and through my online programs, I find that the traditional viewpoints and ways of suppressing symptoms are deeply ingrained and have become a comfortable habit.

Repeating these natural concepts and principles is crucial until your response to health problems is to focus on and MAGNIFY "health" instead of the "problem". Symptoms are not the illness or disease state itself, they are a communication of the condition of the body.

They are a combination of sending an alarm and they also serve as part of the healing process; communicating and clarifying what state the body's in and which direction the body is headed. When recognized and heard, they provide a roadmap to knowing where your horse is, so you can set the compass to where you want them to be.

YOU CAN'T SKIP OR STUFF YOUR HORSE'S EMOTIONS AND EXPECT HEALTH

Emotions are energy in motion and are a result of your or the horse's state, psychology, and feelings. Emotions have the power to create or destroy, and we have the option to choose which. As a horse owner, we can help our horses do the same. Sometimes, we unconsciously encourage or promote negative emotions and patterns in our horses, which can result in less desirable behavior, and can cause health concerns and issues as well.

There are other factors to consider that can influence your horses emotions and patterns, such as **innate characteristics** they were born with. For example, if their mother, or even in later life, herd mates are skeptical and distrusting of people, this can affect the horse's feelings, thoughts, and responses to people.

Environment can play a part as well. What they have been exposed to and even the energy or condition of the surroundings.

Learned behavior and thought patterns. Whether they were from training methods, events, performances, handling, or lack of handling, and so on.

To understand the connection, we need to know how the brain handles emotions. The answer lies in the limbic system. The limbic system is considered the center of emotions in the brain. It has a direct connection to the olfactory nerve, which is responsible for the sense of smell. Have you ever had a smell bring back memories or strike an emotion? This is why.

The limbic system does not just connect and communicate with the olfactory nerve though. It receives input and signals from the entire body and senses. Because of this, a horse that has a pattern of pain, perhaps with a poor fitting saddle or experiences pain at every performance, can associate the event or object with pain. This can have a noticeably negative effect on the horse's behavior and cause the horse to form unhealthy emotional patterns.

Often times even if a pain or stress trigger is removed, the emotional response or pattern can stay, leaving a negative impact on the horse's health, wellness, and behavior. Learning to help the horse process through negative emotional patterns is something all horse owners can learn to do and should, to promote the overall wellbeing of their horse.

WHAT YOU USE ON THE SURFACE COUNTS

In Chapter 2, I mentioned that the ingredients of the products you use on your horse are just as important as the ingredients you put in your horse. What you put on topically will make contact with your horse's largest organ, the skin. The skin serves as your horse's first exterior barrier of protection. Let's discuss a few of the most widely utilized topical products that could negatively impact your horse's health, if you're not aware of the ingredients.

Liniments - Are common for performance horses, some trail horses, horses recovering from injury, and senior horses. What you might not have realized is the ingredients you're rubbing on your horse's coat/skin could be detrimental to their health.

Here is a breakdown of a few of the ingredients found in top-selling liniment products:

Menthol - Is one of the most commonly used ingredients in a majority of chemically-based horse liniment options. Wikipedia gives the perfect definition: "Menthol is an organic compound made synthetically or obtained from corn mint, peppermint or other mint oils." It is considered organic whether it is made synthetically, or obtained from the plant itself. Synthetically made chemicals may resemble the plants organic chemical makeup, but they do not deliver the same benefits in a therapeutic sense. So to achieve the therapeutic benefits of a plant to increase horse health and wellbeing, you are better off using herbs or therapeutic grade essential oils.

Can chemical liniments reduce heat and increase circulation? Yes. Both the true organic source and the synthetic menthol will topically stimulate the skin and act as an analgesic. But that is only "treating" the symptom or increasing circulation; not necessarily supporting horse health and wellness, which is not enough result for me when I am looking to support clients' horses that are hard working athletes, or retired horses suffering from injuries or just worn out. I expect healing and therapeutic results without added toxic chemicals!

Chloroxylenol - Is the next ingredient I would like to break down. It is added as an antimicrobial. Here is an interesting description to think about: though Chloroxylenol is not significantly toxic to humans and other mammals, it's "practically" non-toxic to birds, moderately toxic to freshwater invertebrates and highly toxic to fish. It's a mild skin irritant and may trigger allergic reactions in some individuals. Does that sound like a good fit for improving health?

Acetone - In case you don't recognize the ingredient, it's found in your fingernail polish remover and paint removers. Although considered safe in small amounts, is it something you wish to apply repeatedly to your horse with no added health benefit?

Plant Extracts - Although not a concern to your horse's health, you will see plant extracts added to many products, especially those that claim to be natural. Understand that the therapeutic results you are looking for are not going to be found in extracts. Plant extracts are often used for cooking or for aroma purposes, but not to get a therapeutic effect. Essential oils are extracted from plants, but will not be listed as plant extracts. That being said, even if the ingredient list mentions essential oils, they are rarely therapeutic grade. One way to know is often by price and, in some products, you can tell from aroma.

Just like you can select more natural nutrition, you can do the same with your liniment. Selecting herbal, essential oil, or homeopathic-based liniments will not only improve the effectiveness, but will ensure that you're promoting the overall health and wellbeing of your horse from the outside in.

Fly Spray - The key to effective fly control is to not let them overpopulate in the first place. When you're in places where the population is already a concern, then starting with horse protection or detouring the flies from harassing your horse is beneficial.

Most horse owners head to the tack or feed store and purchase a fly spray off the shelf. The warning labels on the store bought sprays are enough to tell me "No thank you!" Even the ones marketed "natural" are often unbearable in my opinion, and contain synthetics or poor quality ingredients.

Pyrethrum is an extract of chrysanthemum flowers. It contains two naturally occurring insecticides, pyrethrin I and pyrethrin II. Both are approved for use in agriculture, household insecticides, pet flea and tick treatments, for use on livestock, and yes, in our fly sprays for horses.

These chemicals work by disrupting nerve transmission. Absorption through the skin is believed to be minimal, yet known to be easily absorbed through the respiratory system. Little research has been conducted to horse sensitivities or possibe linked health concerns after long-term exposure to and use of these products.

You can instead utilize safer, naturally-based fly sprays or even make your own with therapeutic grade essential oils like Geranium, Eucalyptus, and Lavender, combined with water. Check out the latest ready to order options on the bonus page: **www. equineessentialwellness.com/bookbonus**.

Much like parasite control, it's best to have a control plan in place to keep pesky fly populations down. Try utilizing fly traps, with natural non toxic fly bait' although, beware some of the attractants for these traps are toxic and dangerous for amphibians and fish.

A more enjoyable way of fly control for horses is to get planting. By having some geraniums and marigolds planted around your facility, you can help make the environment around your horses less appealing for flies. You can also talk to your local plant nursery specialist for other options of plants that may be beneficial for pest control. These plants can be toxic if horses eat them, so plant them in spaces the horses can't access.

There's also no denying your manure management is key for fly control! Cleaning pens and/or dragging them is a great way to control the fly breeding environment. Spreading natural fly predators at your main manure pile and the outline of your pens is a great natural way to help prevent the flies from hatching, and makes managing and repelling adults that much easier.

SUMMARY & ACTION STEPS

Hopefully by now you're starting to connect the importance of seeing your horse's health from a big picture, whole horse approach.

This chapter served to tie in some finishing touches and aspects to your horse's health and care that tend to be pushed aside or ignored.

The summary is to listen to your horse's symptoms, honor and recognize their emotions and behavior, and review the ingredients of topical products just as thoroughly as the products you feed.

CHAPTER EIGHT

Natural Modalities to Enhance Health

NO NEED FOR FANCY GADGETS

This chapter will share options of natural remedies and modalities that don't rely on expensive human-made gadgets or elaborate machines to support and improve the health of your horse.

There's a time and place for some of those therapies, but don't underestimate the value of what energy, plants, and simple hands can do!

You can choose to work with professionals certified in these modalities or empower yourself with the information on how to use them yourself through resources like the Horse Health Hub.

You need to ensure that the professional you choose to work with or the approach you take yourself comes from a place of promoting health versus suppressing symptoms. When working with a professional or studying a course, book, or with a mentor, you should be clear on what their views are and what school of thought they subscribe to.

There are two primary schools of thought: rationalist and the empirical. It's important to understand there are varied views and understandings of health and disease. The rationalist school of thought primarily focuses on external pathogens, the disease itself, and the symptoms. Most traditional practitioners and veterinarians have been educated with this theory, even some of the natural or holistic practitioners as well.

The second school of thought is described as the empirical school of thought. Their primary focus is on the terrain of the body. Those who believe and are taught this school of thought also see the mental and emotional patterns as pertinent to health. The symptom is "heard" and, rather than looking to suppress, the practitioner is looking to support the body through, while working to pinpoint the cause of the disruption in health and homeostasis.

Once you have established a foundation of health and secured your horse's firewalls of protection, you can begin in effectively utilizing various natural modalities to benefit and enhance your horse's health. Here's a brief look into a small selection of common natural modalities you could choose to explore for your horse.

Essential Oils - Essential oils are volatile liquids that are extracted from plant material through distillation. If distillation is done properly, they will contain the chemical constituents and characteristics of the plant. There is much to learn and understand in regards to utilizing essential oils for your horse. Just like there are schools of thought for health care practitioners, the same is true for those who use, train, or research the use of essential oils.

There are three schools of thought that are currently prominent with essential oils:

1. **British school of thought** uses more diluted and less "pure" essential oils. Often has many warnings or cautions with certain oils.
2. **German school of thought** tends to lean toward aromatherapy and inhalation of essential oils. Not much belief or use topically or internally.
3. **French school of thought** is considered very open and pure to various uses of essential oils with the use of science to help back it.

Knowing which you believe or concur with, and that of any professional you choose to work with, can lead to better results for your horse. There are many synthetics on the market and ensuring you're using therapeutic grade and pure essential oils is the only way to keep your horse safe, as well as to see the results in which you seek. Because altered or lab created essential oils are not equal and cannot compare to natural and pure essential oils.

Essential oils are potent and should be treated with care, but not fear. Very little is needed and, with the proper understanding and use, they can promote monumental shifts in your horse's health, due to their frequency and ability to access the limbic system.

Flower Essences - Another great option that works with vibrations and frequency is that of flower essences. The vibrational essence is obtained through flower petals. An electrically charged combination of water and preservative, you can utilize the benefits of a flower essence with just a few drops internally or topically. Through harmonizing and enhancing energetic flow and shifting negative or out of sync vibrations these great gifts of nature can support emotional and energetic balance that will promote health and wellness.

For those educated in the history of flower essences, their belief of the cause of disease is a distortion of the wavelength in the energy field of the body. This aligns with the terrain theory, or that of the empirical school of thought discussed earlier, as it looks to the lack of homeostasis and imbalance as the sign of concern and illness.

There are so many ways that our domestic environment disrupts your horse's true nature or way of being. This can bring a negative shift in their energy flow, causing disharmony and opening the door to illness, disease, and behavioral concerns. Flower essences can restore and return your horse to their true nature. Horses often "speak" through their behavior and body language.

Because of this, it's important to observe and understand what is being communicated by the horse. Reading and interpreting the horse's behavior will enable you to move forward with the proper or appropriate flower essence.

Herbs - Although possibly better known and understood, the use of herbs in a true holistic approach requires that the person choosing the herb for the horse recognizes the body as a synergistic whole of connected parts and organ systems and that the symptoms of the body are communications of these systems. It's with this view and understanding that one can clearly move forward to the proper selection and utilization of herbal remedies.

By looking for the source and root of a health concern, one can then try to select herbs much in the way a horse would do if they were in a natural habitat in which they had the freedom to self-treat or medicate themselves. This is not to imply a diagnosis or treatment of those using herbs, just an explanation of how horses would care for themselves without human interaction or impediments.

Homeopathy - Samuel Hahnemann was the founder of Homeopathy. He had a medical degree that he obtained in 1779, after enrollment in medical school in 1775. Being a man torn with what he witnessed and experienced in practice, he went on to utilize his education in chemistry and foreign language to make a living. It was through this work and translations that he came across the idea and principle of the Law of Similars. His work was then furthered by Constantine Hering who authored and contributed to what is known as Hering's Rule of Cure:

"In all chronic and lingering cases the symptoms appearing last, and even though they may appear insignificant, are always important to regard to the selection of a drug; the oldest are the least important... Only such patients remain well and are really cured who have been rid of their symptoms in the reverse order of their development."

The term "homeopathic remedy" is more appropriate as the true purpose and goal is to remedy the situation or cause of concern. Some refer to homeopathic remedies as medicines; they must then take into consideration the traditional view of medicine, which has a primary and secondary effect and tends to simply mask or suppress a symptom. Differing outcomes to the situation or concern at hand, therefore, the term homeopathic remedy is the preferred terminology.

When considering homeopathy as a natural health care option, or seeking out a professional to work with, finding one with an understanding both of the remedies themselves and the process to nature cure is important. Seeking their knowledge or education in the ideas of partial cure, palliation, suppression, non curative aggravation, and natural disease cycles can be beneficial in any natural practitioner or modality professional who you seek to work with.

Iridology - Is the study of the iris, the colored portion of the eye. Dating back as far as 1846, iridology was used by a wide range of people throughout history and was revered or viewed as searching or studying the window of the soul. It was believed through the eye, one's "whole" was seen and could be used as a guide or map to aliments or health concerns in the body; that combined with the fact that the iris is known to reflect specific organ and organ systems within the body.

Through observing and studying the fibers of the iris and color, you can gain insight into the inner workings and condition of the body. This map or guide can bring awareness to weakness or concern inside the body, in which the practitioner or owner applying this modality can then utilize to support the animal's health appropriately.

Like the other modalities shared prior to this, it's the hope to provide awareness and education to the owner, not to diagnose, treat, cure, or prevent any health or medical conditions.

Bodywork - There are diverse methods of bodywork that can be done to promote health. Much like selecting the proper natural remedy, there is much to consider when selecting a bodyworker for your horse. There are options geared more for the athlete, relaxation, circulation, re-balancing energy, and some that can do a little of them all. For the sake of this book, we will introduce massage, acupressure, TTouch, Ortho Bionomy, Reiki, and Equine Touch.

Massage in and of itself can differ greatly in the education and background of the therapist and their preferred style. Some popular types of manipulation are:

- Swedish stroking, which is the use of effleurage. Long, deep, slow cleansing strokes are utilized to warm the muscles. This stroke is a great option to increase circulation and cleanse the body.

- Sports Massage stroking is a more vigorous style of stroking. Using strokes like percussion can create a vibration in the body and awakens and shifts the nervous system, instead of the circulatory system. These types of strokes tend to be relaxing and calming to the horse.

- Cross Fiber strokes create a blood rush to help break up blockage, either a spasm of a trigger point type, or a blockage of a meridian point. They can also be an option to break up adhesions and scar tissue.

Each session should be unique to the horse and many therapists will use intuition to guide their knowledge and understanding of the strokes and anatomy of the horse as they work through the session. Benefits of massage include relaxation of muscles, relief of muscle pain and spasm, improved circulation and lymph flow, the removal and flushing toxins from the system, and enhanced performance and mobility by improving range of motion.

Acupressure - Is a modality that has a foundation in Traditional Chinese Medicine. Practitioners will look at each horse as a whole and take into consideration the mental and emotional health, as well as the environment of the horse as they assess how to support the horse back to a state of health. This is a bodywork modality that focuses on energy balance and flow, through the body's meridians and acupressure points.

The meridian system is responsible for communication between the zang-fu (internal) organs, connection of the entire body, and circulation of chi, blood, and other vital substances. Through observation, listening and smelling, proposing questions, and physical palpation, a horse owner with acupressure knowledge or a qualified practitioner can examine the horse. During the physical palpation stage, there are acupressure points that will be assessed.

Their classifications include:

- Association points, back transporting or back-shu points that run along or close to the spine.

- Alarm points, or front Mu points, which will further identify the depth and nature of the animal's imbalance.

There is much to understand and appreciate about this modality. Horse owners interested can learn more about it, or locate a certified and experienced practitioner near them to utilize the benefits and further details of Traditional Chinese Medicine and Acupressure.

TTouch - The TTouch method was developed by Linda Tellington-Jones and has been organized over the history of its use into 15 hand movements and positions that help to reduce stress, enhance relaxation, awareness, and the ability to learn. Depending on the movement the TTouch can be applied by circles, lifts, and slides across the hair. Over the years of practice this method has provided amazing results for many animal species. It is an effective option to support the health and even positive behavior of your horse.

Reiki - Is a gentle and non-invasive therapy focused on a holistic system of energy healing and restoration. Its origins are traced back through history to Japan. The intention of a Reiki practitioner is to connect with the healing energy of the universe and channel it through their hands. Seeking to balance the flow of the energy of the body and clear any blockages or disruptions that may be present. Benefiting the mental, emotional, and physical wellbeing of the horse.

Ortho Bionomy - Is a non-invasive system of healing that reminds the body of its natural ability to restore balance. Based upon the simple principle and belief that the body can correct and balance itself, when given the right space and input to do so.

The founder, British-trained Osteopath Arthur Lincoln Pauls, discovered how to gently stimulate the body's reflexes for self-correction in a way that supports the body's own healing mechanisms. First primarily practiced on people, there is a growing awareness and appreciation of this work in the horse industry.

Through an Ortho Bionomy session, the horse's body is stimulated using gentle movements, comfortable positioning, brief compression and subtle contact. The result is seemingly effortless natural re-alignment, relaxation, and the health benefits that follow.

Equine Touch - Is a non-diagnostic, non-invasive equine bodywork system that utilizes a very specific move focused on working with soft tissue, affecting mostly connective tissue – muscles and tendons, joint capsules and ligaments.

With a combination of stimulated meridians, muscle, and fascia, Equine Touch brings the benefits of both physical bodywork and energy work together in a modality that can support the horse's body in regaining or maintaining flow, balance, and harmony.

SUMMARY & ACTION STEPS

Referring to the bonus page, we have a link to additional information on finding practitioners of these modalities, and even learning how to do some of the work yourself.

Through the basic explanation of the natural modalities above, horse owners can explore and choose the best option for their horse, based on the needs and the situation. Each option is unique and has its own benefits and characteristics in regards to boosting the health and wellness of your horse.

CHAPTER NINE

Customization

WHY COOKIE CUTTER APPROACHES TO HEALTH FAIL

When a horse is experiencing a health condition or concern, the cause is unique to them as an individual. Your horse's genetics, history, lifestyle, and current state of health all serve a crucial role in understanding why they're experiencing the problems they are. If your horse is healthy, these are still important factors that can shed light on what areas of weakness your horse might have and what they are susceptible to.

We've explored cell health and its importance in relation to your horse's health. Another aspect of cellular health that's important to understand when looking to customize health is the categories and synergies that take place within the body. Seeing connections you might not have realized existed before.

Groups of like cells performing a common function are called tissues, and groups of like tissues form organs. Understanding the different body tissue types found in our horses can give insight to more accurately gauge damage and healing time of each illness or injury.

There are five tissue groups to be aware of, to gain a better comprehension of the connection and synergy of the body as a whole.

Epithelial Tissue - Covers all body surfaces both inside and out, including body cavities, surfaces of blood vessels, and organs. Although epithelial tissues do not have a direct blood supply, they regenerate quickly when damaged. They receive their nutrients from underlying connective tissues, on which they are anchored. All glands are made of epithelial tissues. The function of these tissues include secretion, transcellular transport, selective absorption, protection, and sensing. This is a general understanding of this tissue group, it's further divided and classified according to the various shapes and functions.

Connective Tissue - Is found throughout the body and it connects, supports, or binds other tissues and organs together. They are classified by their structural characteristics and can include ligaments, tendons, bone, cartilage, and other connective tissues.

Muscle Tissue - Including smooth muscle, cardiac muscle, and skeletal muscle are unlike any other tissue because they have the capacity to contract and relax.

Neural Tissue - Is composed of nerve cells, aka neurons. These tissues are found in the brain, spinal cord, and peripheral nerves.

Organs and Organ Systems - Groups of like cells performing a particular function make up specific organs and organ systems. Each of these must function together in a state of homeostasis. If this state is disrupted, disease will occur.

Having an awareness of these tissue groups illustrates the connection of cells, tissues, and organs to your horse's health. Disease, in a traditional sense, is often narrowed down to a dysfunctional organ or organ system. This dysfunction will have a ripple effect on the entire body.

In a moment, we will discuss areas of concern and how they will relate to your horse individually as you promote their health naturally. First, I would like you to take a look at and understand the vital organ systems that could be an area of concern for your horse.

THE REMARKABLE SYNERGY OF YOUR HORSE'S BODY

The Digestive System - We explored the basics of the digestive system in Chapter 3, but as a refresher, bear in mind that Hippocrates once said *"All disease begins in the gut."*... So the GI tract has a synergistic link to the overall health of all systems within the body.

In this chapter, I want to explore some additional concepts of the digestive system that you can utilize to customize care for your horse. We talked about the traditional understanding of the digestive system in Chapter 3, but when I discovered and explored the Traditional Chinese Medicine (TCM) view of the digestive system, new understandings came to light that help me "hear" each horse's body in a deeper way.

What stood out to me about the view of the digestive system with TCM is partly the view of the Spleen. Maybe you've had a horse that regardless of what you do, they fail to gain or maintain weight. They sometimes have with that concern: stifle weakness, are lethargic, have a compromised immune system, and tend to be anxious, or off in another world and lacking focus. It's possible that concerns are more present at a certain time of year or get worse in certain climate conditions.

I saw this time and time again with horse owner after horse owner… And when I began factoring in TCM and bringing balance to otherwise ignored energetic and physical organ systems of the body, results with these horses increased dramatically. The Spleen, in the context of TCM, doesn't necessarily correspond to the anatomical part called the spleen. Instead, it refers to a functional and energetic entity and aspect associated with the stomach.

Together with the stomach, the spleen regulates the absorption of food and the dispersal of food's nutritive essence throughout the body, sending the morbid/waste fluids to the kidneys and bladder.

The Spleen wasn't the only area of new awareness and results that was discovered. In TCM, the Liver, Gallbladder, Large Intestine, and Small Intestine are also part of the digestive system. Now you might be thinking… Hold your horses, woman! Horses DON'T have a gallbladder. I understand that physically your horse doesn't have a gallbladder organ. And yet, in TCM, they still have a Gallbladder Meridian and if you think about it, the body still has the "function" of a gallbladder; it's simply completed within the liver.

In TCM, the Liver and Gallbladder are connected sister meridians. While reading about a horse getting worse during a certain time of year or weather, you might have been thinking that although your horse does experience worse conditions, the condition is more related to muscle cramps or stiffness, tendon or ligament issues, joint problems, hoof issues, eye or vision concerns, or maybe your horse's behavior seems depressed, aggressive, irritable, or unpredictable.

Even some horses that appear to be experiencing nervous systems concerns, that stumble or lack coordination have benefited and improved in health when the Liver and Gallbladder were stimulated and brought back into balance.

What about the small intestine? In TCM, the Small Intestine is referred to as the Official Who Separates the Pure from the Impure. It serves to separate and aid in keeping the body pure of impurities. For horses that have dental concerns, TMJ pain or tension, and nutrient absorption issues, combined with other digestive concerns, this would be an area to explore and balance.

Finally, we come to the Large Intestine, which in TCM, serves as a support and sidekick to the Lung. Promoting both respiratory function and immune strength.

Physically, the large intestine does receive processed food from the small intestine. Aiding in both absorption of nutrients and secretion of waste, the large intestine plays a crucial role in digestive health and function.

What I appreciate and value from the TCM view that is often left out from other beliefs and modalities is the energetic component of the Large Intestine. The Large Intestine serves as an energetic cleanser and processor, alongside the work it does with digested food matter.

The Large Intestine is another place in which prolonged grief can be stored or back up, if not processed properly. With behavioral expressions to reflect this back up including things like being stubborn or resistant, and even times of compulsive, or what seems like uncontrollable behaviors.

Gaining this deeper understanding has empowered me to guide horse owners to results they haven't achieved before. Simply because we are now listening to the body, hearing what it says, and doing a much more thorough job of interpreting and supporting the body back to health and balance; instead of the traditional shrugging of shoulders or suppression of symptoms with no regard to what area of the body is seeking assistance.

The Respiratory System - The Master of the Pulse, that's what the lungs are referred to in TCM. Yes, the Lung and the entire respiratory system work together with both the cardiovascular and hematopoietic systems to provide the body with the proper exchange of oxygen and carbon dioxide. This connection and synergy between systems explains the importance of homeostasis and the severe domino effect that can take place when dysfunction occurs.

Ultimately, the chief and master that allows the pulse is the Lung. Of course, the Heart plays a major role and function for the body. But, for now, I hope you can appreciate that the Lung - both meridian and organ system - is far more than just what we observe with the rise and fall of the breath.

Opening your awareness to all these synergistic partnerships within the body awakens the value of every communication the body expresses. Everything means something. The more subtle cues and signs you choose to listen to, the better off your horse will be.

The Cardiovascular System - Consisting of the heart and blood vessels, which carry oxygen-rich blood to both nourish and cleanse the body. Followed with the hematopoietic system is the bodily system primarily involved in the production of blood. Not a commonplace topic in general horse health care.

If your horse has experienced heart murmurs or arrhythmia, it's possible you further explored this area of health for your horse… But, typically, those conditions are considered uncommon. That doesn't mean that there aren't imbalances or concerns within this system happening without such problems.

In TCM, the Heart is referred to as the Supreme Controller, and the Pericardium is known to be the protector or guardian of the Heart. You don't have to fully understand all the connections or have them memorized to raise your awareness to the fact they exist and need to be recognized.

Imbalances or restricted energetic flow of these areas could present with behavioral concerns, such as difficulty bonding or being timid. It can physically be seen as soreness in the forelimbs or shoulders, suspected chest pain or tension. Other signs could include excessive sweating, brain and nervous system disorders.

The Lymphatic System - A network of tissues, glands, organs, and vessels that rid the body of toxins and is primarily responsible for the immunity of the body. This system requires movement and motion (exercise) from the body in order to properly function. The lymph vessels and volume are twice that of blood. Swollen lymph nodes can be a sign of toxin build up and/or health concern. The function of the lymphatic system can impact and affect various organ systems of the body including endocrine, reproductive, hematopoietic, cardiovascular, and digestive systems.

TCM doesn't recognize the lymphatic system in the same way, but the Triple Heater Meridian and understanding is where you can seek to best support and balance a horse that is experiencing imbalance or sluggish flow within the lymphatic system.

The Triple Heater serves to bring balance and harmony to the body. It assists in being a thermoregulator. Horses experiencing metabolic concerns, climate sensitivity, and hormone imbalance can benefit greatly from supporting the Triple Heater.

The Musculoskeletal System - Includes muscle, bone, and connective tissue which offers protection to vital organs, such as the brain, spinal cord, and so on. The most common concern I am contacted about regarding the musculoskeletal system is related to connective tissue health and support. Horse tendon injuries and conditions can be a common concern and issue for performance horses.

Promoting proper health and wellness for equine tendons is important and should include proper fitness and adequate, clean nutrition.

Tendons are flexible but inelastic cords of strong fibrous collagen tissue attaching a muscle to a bone. Ligaments are a short band of tough, flexible, fibrous connective tissue that connects two bones or cartilages, or holds together a joint.

Depending on the type of concern and the horse's specific history, you can seek to support the Stomach, Spleen, Small Intestine, Liver, or Gallbladder to benefit and promote the health of this system.

The Nervous System - The hub of maintaining homeostasis of the body. Many bodily functions and actions take place because of neural stimulation. It's important to note that both muscle and nerve cells require a great deal of energy to function properly, so they can be impacted first when nutrition and oxygen intake is not adequate.

The Endocrine System - Works with the nervous system to regulate the body's functions and activity. The Endocrine system includes the thyroid gland, parathyroid gland, adrenal glands, pituitary gland, and the pineal gland. This system controls hormones and specialized communication of the body.

The Reproductive System - Operates in synergy with the endocrine system. The health of these two systems are greatly entwined. The hormone creation and balance of the body has limitless effects on the function and health of the reproductive system.

In TCM, the endocrine and reproductive systems are balanced by the Kidney Meridian. The Kidney Meridian is the River of Life as it serves as the source of Original Chi. This chi (force of life and vitality) is passed down from your horse's dam and shire. This life force is given at birth and the strength, flow, and amount of the Original Chi determines the confirmation, vitality, and longevity the horse will have.

The Urinary System - Anatomically includes the kidneys and bladder, which serve to rid your horse's body of morbid waste that remains from the process of food matter being transformed into energy and nutrients.

This system regulates the optimal balance of water and electrolytes within the body; while serving a crucial role in the production of hormones that aid in maintaining healthy blood pressure, producing blood cells, and proper salt absorption.

Although we talked about the role of the Kidney in TCM in regards to the endocrine and reproductive systems, both the Kidney and Bladder Meridians are supported and addressed when a horse is experiencing imbalance within the urinary system.

SUMMARY & ACTION STEPS

The more horses I work with, the more this theory seems to ring true. Each horse appears to have what I like to call an area of concern. This is an organ or system that tends to be at risk more than the others. It is different and specific to each horse.

Although there are people who have categorized it some by breed or the horse's personality, I prefer to look at the horse purely as an individual. To give an example, if your horse seems susceptible or prone to getting heaves when they are stressed. Another example is prone to hives, or colic. Tracking and being aware of your horse's tendencies can help you more effectively prepare and care for their individual needs.

This synergy is shared in hopes of bringing awareness, so that as symptoms arise in any of these given areas, you can use the other information shared in this book to know what the body may be trying to communicate, as well as where future indications might occur if not cared for or suppressed.

Teaching and empowering you to customize your horse's care is not something I believe can be done within the constructs of a book... You have all the information you need to develop a care plan for your horse that develops amazing health and vitality.

If you wish to take what you've learned and individualize more to your horse's needs, please check out the Horse Health Hub Online Resource - **www.horsehealthhub.com.**

The journey to your horse's health begins here and now! I hope this resource serves you well in transforming your horse's health through a natural, effective framework of care.

REFERENCES

Chapter 1 -

Chan, Melissa. "Veterinarians Face Unique Issues That Make Suicide One of the Profession's Big Worries". Time Magazine, September 12, 2019: Website.

Tunsky, Gary. (2010). "The Battle for Health is Over pH Life and Death Hangs in the Balance". Black Mountain, NC: Crusader Enterprises: Pages 13-17.

Chapter 2 -

Oke, Stacey, DVM, MSC. "What is Nutrigenomics". theHorse.com, April 7, 2014: Website.

Chapter 3 -

Oke, Stacey, DVM MSC. "Exploring the Equine Microbiome". theHorse.com, August 2016: Pages 26-30.

Chapter 4 -

Jacobs, Dennis E. (2015). "Principles of Veterinary Parasitology". Chichester, West Sussex: Wiley Blackwell.

Ramey, David, DVM. ""Natural" Dewormers". doctorramey.com, January 19, 2019: Website.

Author not listed. "Alternative lice remedies tested, Tea tree and lavender oil prove effective in treating lice". EQUUS Magazine, July 25, 2019: Website.

Chapter 6 -

Cook, R. and Strasser, H. (2003). "Metal in the Mouth – The Abusive Effects of Bitted Bridles". Published by Sabine Kells, Canada.

Ramey, P. (2003). "Wild Health. Making Natural Hoof Care Work for You". Star Ridge Publishing,Fayetteville, AR.

Christenson, D. (2009). "Veterinary Medical Terminology", Second Edition. St. Louis, MO: Saunders Elsevier

ABOUT THE AUTHOR

Angie Wells is a Horse Health Coach whose vision is to improve the quality of life and health for horses utilizing natural approaches to care. Focusing strongly on health instead of disease to maximize results.

Combining her background and experience as a Certified Equine Massage Therapist, Equine Sports Trainer, Equine Naturopath, Equine Acupressure Practitioner, and lifelong learner.

Angie provides both in person body work and horse health coaching sessions alongside online courses and programs to empower horse owners with the tools, skills, and information they need to customize their horse's health and care specific to the individual horse's needs and preferences.

She has been successfully supporting horses professionally since 2003 and now serves an international base of horse owners through her education programs and services offered through her business, Equine Essential Wellness.

Made in the USA
Las Vegas, NV
18 November 2020

11077433R10068